Speaking of Women's Health

RECIPES FOR LIVING WELL

THE BOOK

OUR "RECIPES" FOR HEALTH, WELL-BEING
AND PERSONAL SAFETY

2004

Introduction

"RECIPES" FOR LIVING WELL

*W*hat is a recipe? OK, technically, it's a list of ingredients and directions describing how to put those ingredients together to create something wonderful! But what makes a recipe special? Is it knowing that it was given to you by a cherished grandmother, mom, aunt or best friend? Is it remembering with whom you enjoyed that meal so much? Is it actually making the food together with your friends or family, or is it that first time you allowed your child to stir the pancake batter or pour the cereal "all by herself"? In fact, it may even be having your kids come home from school and follow your instructions for fixing a nutritious frozen dinner so it's ready when you come home from work!

Of course, great recipes are about great food and living well. There are other **"recipes for living well"** that may **enhance your entire sense of well-being.** It, too, is all about ingredients and "putting it together". Reducing stress is certainly a "recipe" for more happiness and less disease. Exercise is a "recipe" for less body fat, lower cholesterol, and a better balance (and about 20 other benefits, too). Partnering with your doctor and scheduling regular screenings is a "recipe" for a longer, healthier, happier life. Eating the right foods (including some chocolate) may be a "recipe" for avoiding heart disease, osteoporosis, cancers and even the common cold.

So why, when we already know most of this, do we ignore so many of these "recipes for living well"? Perhaps, it is because we are leaving out the most essential "ingredient" of all.....Passion!

Let's think about those food recipes, again. Think how delighted we are when we make a great meal, serve it and watch our guests (and let's not forget ourselves) ooh and aah about how it looks and smells and tastes.....we savor every bite.....that's the passion. And, that success certainly encourages us to make that recipe again, and do it with style! In this book, "Recipes for Living Well", because it is the mission of Speaking of Women's Health, we will help you put the passion into health, well-being and personal safety. We'll help you create that day-to-day passion that comes from within and thrives when nurtured. We hope this book gives you your first success and encourages you to continue the joy. We want you to savor that kind of success in your everyday health, well-being and personal safety, because, once again, that is the mission of Speaking of Women's Health. "Recipes for Living Well, The Book" will help you put passion into living well.

"Recipes For Living Well" will make you feel excited about your own possibilities, and it will give you ideas about sharing the joy of living well.

Inside, you will find cooking recipes from Speaking of Women's Health Celebrities and National Sponsor Associates. In some cases, our Speakers, who are our experts, have also given some "recipes for living well".

A million thanks for putting your trust in Speaking of Women's Health. We put our trust in you, too.

With best wishes for successful "recipes",

The Staff at
Speaking of Women's Health

This book is designed to provide information about health, not medical advice. Please consult your physician if you have any questions or concerns.

Table of Contents

Letter of Introduction 2

Chapter 1 **Staying Healthy** 6
Blueberry Burgers 17
Blueberry Cobbler 19

Chapter 2 **Recipe for a Healthy Heart** 20
Guacamole Dip 31
Salmon 33

Chapter 3 **Strong Bones** 34
Mac & Cheese 43
Lentil Soup 45

Chapter 4 **Exercise** 46
BLT Salad 59
Shrimp Pasta 61

Chapter 5 **Mental Health** 62
Chicken Cacciatore 73
Thanksgiving Day Turkey 75

Chapter 6 **Build Relationships
Your Heart Desires** 76
Apple Crisp 85
Chocolate Mint Cake 87

Chapter 7 **Trust Your Gut** 88
Pork Loin with Cherry Stuffing 99
Brown Rice Medley 101

Chapter 8 **Sandwich Generation** 102
Chick Pea and Corn Patties 113
Marinated Flank Steak 115

Chapter 9 **Pretty Is as Pretty Does** 116
Spring Salad 129
Salsa 131

Chapter 10 **Healthy Screenings** 132
Peruvian Chicken 139
Marsala Winter Vegetables 141

Index 142

Speaking of Women's Health "Recipes for Living Well, The Book" is meant to increase your knowledge of current developments in women's health. In no way, however, are any of the suggestions in this book meant to take the place of advice given by your licensed health care professionals. Consult your physician or other licensed health care professional before commencing any medical treatment or exercise program. Speaking of Women's Health doesn't make any claims or endorsements for any products, services or procedures which appear in this book.

The Cleveland Clinic Foundation is pleased to support Speaking of Women's Health by contributing the nutritional analyses for the recipes in this book, "Recipes for Living Well – The Book". Speaking of Women's Health and Cleveland Clinic Foundation have a rich history of partnering in several ways. We host both Speaking of Women's Health and Universal Sisters conferences in Cleveland, Ohio and Miami, Florida. At the Cleveland Clinic, we believe *"Every Life Deserves World-Class Care"*, and are proud to announce a new joint effort with Speaking of Women's Health: a first-ever physician education landmark event. The two-day First Annual Women's Health Summit is a Continuing Medical Education (CME) conference April, 2005. This CME educates about an interdisciplinary approach to caring for female patients in areas such as cardiovascular disease, breast care and imaging, incontinence, pelvic floor disorders, minority health and new technologies. We invite interested physicians and health care professionals to visit the website at www.clevelandclinicmeded.com/women.htm.

With all of this collaboration, it seemed a perfect fit for Cleveland Clinic Foundation to lend its nutritional resources to Speaking of Women's Health. Speaking of Women's Health is a unique organization that has emerged as a valuable resource for women in America. We are proud to work with Speaking, and to provide you with information to help you make healthy choices for your nutrition.

For more information and a link to free, personalized nutrition guidance from the Cleveland Clinic Heart Center, ranked number one in the United States for the past ten years by *U.S. News & World Report*, log on to www.speakingofwomenshealth.com/main.asp, and click on the e-Cleveland Clinic link. This will take you to the e-Cleveland Clinic Web page to discover how your own personalized, on-line dietitian-guided healthy-eating plan can help you look better, feel better, and improve your health and well-being for years to come.

Enjoy this book, enjoy your health, enjoy your life!

Cleveland Clinic Foundation

Chapter 1

Staying Healthy

The aim of life is to live,

and to live means to be aware,

joyously, serenely, divinely aware.

Henry Miller

Our recipe for living well
begins very simply...

Stay Healthy

and be aware!

Your body is made of more than 50 trillion cells, 650 muscles and 206 bones, all powered by a heart that beats close to 36 million times each year. You breathe in and out more than 23,000 times a day, and in the seconds it will take you to finish reading this sentence your eyes will perform 10 billion computer-like calculations. What does it take to power this complex and miraculous activity machine? The answer is simple...Nutrition!

Do you eat to live or live to eat?

In earlier times, eating was simple. Most people grew their own foods. They ate when they were hungry and worked their fields, daily, for exercise. Today, life is different. We have multiple food choices and options. This can be a very good thing, but...it can also be a challenge.

The key to a healthy diet is simple. Eat plenty of fruits and vegetables (fresh, when convenient), include whole grains in your diet, eat more fish and seafood and choose lean meats and low-fat dairy products. Use herbs, spices and healthy condiments to add flavor and help maintain the naturally-occurring nutrients.

There are six basic "ingredients" your body needs – protein, carbohydrates, fats, vitamins, minerals and WATER!

Protein

Protein is essential for growth, and, next to water, is the largest component in the body. Protein builds and repairs skin, bones, muscles, organs and blood while assisting functions such as immunity, hormone production, blood clotting and water balance. A healthy diet should include a daily caloric intake that is made of 10 to 20% protein.

The best way to ensure your weekly diet provides enough protein is to include the following, as part of a balanced diet. Good sources of protein, and recommended portions include:

Fish – 5 to 6 ounces, at least twice each week, to provide protein, iron, vitamins and minerals to help prevent disease. Fish is typically low in fat, and some have the added benefit of being high in Omega-3 and Omega-6 fatty acids. Omega fatty acids have been found to help lower heart disease and risk for stroke. Read all of the information about fish on page 27, and see our Salmon recipe on page 33.

Lean meat and poultry – Again, 5 or 6 ounce portions daily for its protein, iron, vitamins and minerals. For red meats, particularly beef, choose lean cuts. Chicken has an abundance of niacin, which may help reduce cholesterol levels, and also contains the easily-absorbed form of iron that provides us with maximum energy and vitality.

Dairy products – Eat at least 2 servings of dairy each day as part of a calcium-rich diet. Choose reduced-fat or non-fat products when possible, to keep your calories and fat in check. One serving of dairy is one 8 oz. cup of fat-free milk or 2 oz. of cheese, or one 8 oz. serving of low-fat yogurt. See page 41 for additional sources of calcium.

Legumes – These are seeds which are harvested from pod-bearing plants. They include peas, beans, lentils, peanuts and soy food products. Legumes are full of protein and are also a powerhouse of energy-producing carbohydrates and fiber. Soy food products contain phytochemicals and soy protein that may help lower cholesterol, build bone mass and may even help reduce the risk of prostate cancer.

Carbohydrates

Much is being debated about carbohydrates…Read this entire paragraph before you run to call us!

Our bodies' main source of energy comes from carbs, and they should make up 50 to 55% of your diet. **We're not talking about simple carbs,** which include sugars and contain no additional nutrients. In general, simple carbs are empty calories. **Complex** *carbohydrates* should be the primary source of carbs in your diet. These include fruits, vegetables and whole grains, which supply important vitamins, minerals and fiber. Complex carbs break down slowly in your body and boost your blood sugar gradually, giving you a steady supply of energy rather than a quick boost.

Rethink your definition of carbohydrates…Some important sources of complex carbs include:

Fruits – citrus, berries, melons, figs, bananas, pumpkin…fruits are "nature's health food". They're convenient and ready to eat and full of healthy nutrients. Eat 3 servings of fruit daily, as a minimum.

Vegetables – including greens, broccoli, celery, carrots, corn, onions, tomatoes, squash, asparagus and beets…these colorful, delicious and extremely versatile foods help maintain optimal health. Eat 3 servings of vegetables daily, as a minimum. Choose fresh or frozen veggies when possible, and prepare in healthy ways – steamed, raw, baked or broiled…avoid overcooking which can deplete the nutrients from the vegetables.

Grains – eat 5 to 6 one-half cup servings daily, preferably whole grain and/or fortified cereals, unbleached or whole wheat flour, brown rice rather than white.

Fats

Given all of the "bad" things we hear about fats, many women are surprised to know that fats are an essential component of a healthy diet. Fats provide energy, insulate against extreme temperatures, protect our organs and help keep our skin healthy. According to the US Food & Drug Administration (FDA), up to 30% of our daily caloric intake should come from fats, with no more than 10% of our calories coming from saturated fats. The key, however, is to choose healthy fats…these include:

- Mono-unsaturated and poly-unsaturated fats – These are found in vegetable and seed oils (think olive and sesame), as well as in nuts and seeds.
- Omega fatty acids – Also referred to as Essential Fatty Acids, Omega-3s are found in some fish (tuna, salmon, mackerel and haddock) and flaxseed, and have been shown to lower heart disease and stroke risk. Omega-6s are found in cereals, whole grain breads, vegetable oils, eggs and poultry. These fats have been shown to reduce inflammation and regulate blood pressure and heart function.

Note:
Saturated fats come from animals and raise our cholesterol. These should be eaten in minimal quantities. Researchers and physicians also feel that hydrogenated fats (trans fatty acids), which are man-made substances, can clog arteries and raise cholesterol.

$\mathcal{I}$t's In The Cards

Deal yourself a good hand. A healthy portion is about equal in size to a "deck of cards".
Is it possible that good nutrition is in the cards or available through palm reading?

Nutritionists and dietitians have found this to be an easy way to communicate "portion size". So, deal yourself a good hand.

Another visual image for portion control is "does it fit in the palm of your hand?" If each serving on your plate is no larger than a deck of cards and will fit into your palm, you probably have a "winning hand".

Need another card trick? Think "sleight (yes, this spelling is correct) of hand". Reduce calories by serving yourself a "slightly" smaller portion than usual.

As always, we strongly suggest reading food labels. Making informed decisions about your diet will have definite health benefits for you and your family.

Water

Water is an essential element for survival, and helps ensure the function of the entire body system. The average person loses about 2% of their body weight in excretions (urine, sweat, etc.) every day. That's about 1 ½ quarts of water. To replace those fluids, drink at least 8 glasses of water a day. The good news is….water is fat-free, has no calories and is conveniently located just about everywhere!

Improving your nutrition does not have to be difficult. Start with one of these suggestions.

1. **Keep a bowl of fresh fruit available.** If it's there, you're more likely to eat it.
2. **Eat breakfast.** Spreading your food intake over the day is the best way to burn calories.
3. **Plan ahead for routine meals and snacks.** People who eat regular meals or use healthy nutritional replacements or supplements get a healthier, more balanced diet and are closer to their weight goals.
4. **Pack your lunch the night before.** If you have a freezer at your workplace, consider buying several frozen meals at a time (put your name on them!). Another choice for women on-the-go might be a nutrition drink or health bar.
5. **Buy a healthy cookbook or food magazine.** If you like to cook, this can help inspire you to cook healthier foods and meals.

How much is enough?

Throughout this book, we will remind you to watch your portion sizes. Read the side panel to the right for some examples of what a "serving" really means. Read the side panel on page 10 for some tricks to help you visualize a healthy portion of food. Also, remember, when eating out, a portion is not necessarily everything that comes on your plate. Enjoy the first part, then take the rest home to share.

Let food be thy medicine.

-Hippocrates

Even with the best of intentions to maintain a healthy diet, our bodies are sometimes susceptible to disease. Whether it's cancer, heart disease, diabetes, osteoporosis, digestive disorders, or the common cold…a nutritional boost may be a great help to prevent or relieve discomfort. Foods are packed with vitamins and nutrients that can help us heal, boost our immune systems, prevent disease, and even elevate our moods. Throughout this book, we'll focus on some of the most-common health issues and how dietary adjustments can influence our bodies' ability to stay healthy or regain health. Even so, it's still essential to talk to your doctor about the latest up-to-date medical treatments and advances. Dietary supplements and healthy eating are one part of a total strategy that you and your health care team should put into place when risk factors are present for disease.

A Healthy Portion or Serving is...

Don't be overwhelmed when you hear that you should eat a minimum of 6 servings of fruits and vegetables each day. Choosing any healthy portion is this easy...

Fruits
One serving of fruit is… $\frac{1}{2}$ cup chopped fruit or 1 medium piece of fruit, $\frac{3}{4}$ cup juice or $\frac{3}{4}$ ounce of dried fruit (this is about one handful).

Veggies
1 cup raw green leaves or $\frac{1}{2}$ cup cooked or raw veggies, or $\frac{3}{4}$ cup of juice.

Grains
1 cup cereal or 1 slice whole wheat bread, $\frac{1}{2}$ cup cooked rice or grain or $\frac{1}{2}$ cup pasta.

Fish, meat, poultry or legumes
1 serving (3 oz.) cooked fish, beef or other meat or $\frac{1}{2}$ cup legumes.

Fat
1 teaspoon butter or oil, 1 tablespoon regular salad dressing, 1 teaspoon peanut butter, $\frac{1}{2}$ ounce nuts.

Dairy
1 cup fat-free or 1% milk, 1 cup fat-free or low-fat yogurt, or 1 ounce cheese.

FOODS THAT HEAL...
what to eat when

The charts on the following pages may help you develop a passion for tailoring a diet specific to your health needs.

To build strong bones, your body needs...

Vitamin A and beta-carotene
Sources include deep orange fruits, orange winter squash, carrots, broccoli, dark green leafy vegetables, liver, low-fat milk, eggs

Calcium
Low or fat-free dairy products, broccoli, dark green leafy vegetables, sardines and salmon with bones, calcium-fortified foods

Vitamin D
Fatty fish, such as herring, salmon and sardines, egg yolks, fortified milk and cereals

Vitamin K
Broccoli, Brussels sprouts, dark green leafy vegetables, liver, legumes, eggs

Manganese
Pineapple, sweet potatoes, spinach, chick peas, whole grains, brown rice, nuts, seeds

Phytoestrogens
Flaxseed, edamame (green soybeans boiled in their pods), other soy products

Zinc
Lean meats, liver, seafood, poultry, lentils, whole grains, wheat germ, buckwheat, Brazil nuts

If you're feeling especially stressed, your body needs...

Vitamin B$_6$
Bananas, figs, prunes, potatoes, chick peas, cauliflower, fortified cereals

Biotin
Soybeans, liver, fish, egg yolks, whole grains

Carbohydrates (unrefined)
All fruits and vegetables, legumes, buckwheat, whole grain foods, brown rice, bran

Fluids
Water, fruit juices, herbal tea

Iron
Dried fruit, dark green leafy vegetables, lean red meats, poultry, seafood, legumes, eggs, fortified cereals

Niacin
Lean meats, fish, canned tuna, legumes, nuts, fortified cereals, whole grain breads

Pantothenic acid
Avocados, broccoli, mushrooms, legumes, meats, whole grain cereals

Potassium
Fresh fruit, dried fruit, prune juice, vegetables, lean meats, seafood, legumes, milk

To help protect against heart disease and diabetes, your body needs...

Vitamin C
Cantaloupe, strawberries, citrus fruits, citrus fruit juices, cranberry juice, tropical fruits, dark green leafy vegetables, cruciferous vegetables (broccoli, cauliflower, cabbage)

Anthocyanins
Berries – blackberries, blueberries, strawberries, raspberries, cranberries, grapes, cherries

Carbohydrates (unrefined)
All fruits and vegetables, legumes, buckwheat, whole grain foods, brown rice, bran

Chromium
Grapefruit, broccoli, fortified breakfast cereals

Vitamin E
Dark green leafy vegetables; vegetable oils such as cotton seed, peanut, sunflower, and safflower; wheat germ; nuts; seeds; whole grain cereals

Fiber
Fruit (especially with skin), dried fruits, vegetables, cruciferous vegetables, legumes, whole grains and cereals, oats and oat bran products, brown rice

Vitamin B6
Bananas, figs, prunes, potatoes, chick peas, cauliflower, fortified cereals

Lycopene
Tomatoes and tomato products, guavas

Folate
Fruits, dark green leafy vegetables, legumes

Omega-3 fatty acids
Fish (including anchovies), bluefish, herring, salmon, sardines, trout, canned light tuna, canola oil, flaxseed oil, flaxseed

Magnesium
Root vegetables, dark green leafy vegetables, seafood, legumes, whole grains, wheat germ, brown rice, ready-to-eat cereals, nuts, seeds

Mono-unsaturated fats
Avocados, olives, olive oil, canola oil, nuts

Potassium
Fresh fruit, dried fruit, prune juice, vegetables, lean meats, seafood, legumes, milk

To guard against cancer, your body needs...

Allyl sulfides
Garlic

Beta-carotene
Deep orange fruits, tropical fruits, deep orange winter squash, carrots and carrot juice, broccoli, dark green leafy vegetables

Vitamin C
Cantaloupe, strawberries, citrus fruits, citrus fruit juices, cranberry juice, tropical fruits, dark green leafy vegetables, cruciferous vegetables

Calcium
Low-fat or fat-free dairy products, broccoli, dark green leafy vegetables, sardines and salmon with bones, calcium-fortified foods

Catechins
Green tea

Chlorogenic acid
Pineapple, strawberries, tomatoes, carrots, green bell peppers

Coumaric acid
Pineapple, strawberries, tomatoes, carrots, green bell peppers

Vitamin E
Dark green leafy vegetables; vegetable oils such as cotton seed, peanut, sunflower, and safflower; wheat germ; nuts; seeds; whole grain cereals

Fiber
Fruits (especially with skin), dried fruits, vegetables, cruciferous vegetables, legumes, whole grains and cereals, oats and oat bran products, brown rice

Folate
Fruits, dark green leafy vegetables, legumes

Indoles
Broccoli, Brussels sprouts, cabbage, Daikon radish

Isothiacyanate (mustard oils)
Watercress, broccoli

Lignans
Flaxseed, flaxseed oil, rye or whole grain crackers

Lycopene
Tomatoes and tomato products, guava

Phenols
Olives, wine

Selenium
Broccoli, fish, seafood, lean meats, chicken, bulgur, whole grain cereals and breads, barley, Brazil nuts

Anthocyanins
Blackberries, blueberries, strawberries, cherries, grapes

Berry Strong

The secret that makes the blueberry one of nature's strongest antioxidant foods can be found in its deep purple-blue color. It's produced by natural dyes called anthocyanins, which are antioxidants that may help reduce your risk of cancer, as well as arthritis, memory loss and other effects of aging. Why? As we age, there is a battle within the cells of our bodies between the damaging substances called free radicals and the protective antioxidants that fight them. Free radicals attack healthy cells in order to steal oxygen from them. Antioxidants combat the harmful effects of free radicals by neutralizing them. So, treat yourself to an old fashioned Blueberry Cobbler. See recipe at the end of this chapter.

Berry-best Burgers

The Blueberry Burger recipe on the following page is a winner, according to Speaking of Women's Health Honorary Chair, Florence Henderson, who contributed the recipe. Florence, also co-host of Lifetime's Speaking of Women's Health TV show which airs every Saturday morning, adds, "the beauty of adding blueberries, beyond the obvious nutritional benefit, is that they help retain the heat and make the burgers wonderfully juicy. I served them one evening after dark on a porch lighted with candles...no one realized that there were blueberries in their burger! They had to take the burger off the bun and investigate. Everyone was delighted when they saw the perfect berries right in their burger. I bet your family and guests will feel the same way!"

Want To Reduce Your Risk of Cancer and other diseases?

Eat more tomatoes! Research shows that these versatile and delicious fruits (yes, fruits!) contain the antioxidant *lycopene*, which may help protect against such disorders as prostate cancer and heart disease. Lycopene is also responsible for the vibrant red color of tomatoes. Any food that contains tomatoes has lycopene – even ketchup. Lycopene is also found in pink grapefruit, watermelon and guava.

Blueberry Burgers

Thanks to Florence Henderson
National Honorary Chairperson & Co-host, *Lifetime's Speaking of Women's Health*

"*The beauty of this hamburger is that it calls for self-expression. I got this recipe from my friend Jay, who is a contemporary art collector, so he is willing to take a few chances with tradition!!! I love his art and his recipes. I think you will, too.*"

INGREDIENTS

2 lbs	freshly ground beef (chuck) *Substitute any lean beef such as ground round or ground sirloin or even turkey*
1 tsp	Jane's Crazy Salt or salt and pepper to taste
¼ tsp	chili powder
1 tsp	Spice Island "Hamburger Seasoning"
⅛ tsp	cayenne pepper
1 Tbsp	dried minced onion *(a bit more if fresh)*
1 Tbsp	dried parsley flakes *(a bit more if fresh)*
¼ cup	milk *(non-fat)*
¾ cup	blueberries

Healthy Garnishes
Fresh green leaf lettuce
Sliced red or yellow tomatoes
Sliced red onion

*Since this recipe exceeds the recommended percentage of calories from fat, think of this as a special treat.

PREPARATION

- Place ground meat in a large bowl and gently break it up. Add all ingredients except blueberries. When incorporating the seasonings and milk, fold in gently with fingers.
- Add the blueberries, being careful not to mash or break the berries.
- Divide the meat into 8 burgers. When forming the patties, it is very important not to over-handle or press the meat...the less shaping and molding, the juicier the burger.
- Place the burgers on a hot charcoal grill. Never use the spatula to flatten the patties during the cooking and only flip them once. The grill flame should never touch the meat.

NUTRITIONAL ANALYSIS
Servings per recipe: 8
Per serving:
335 calories (does not include garnish or bun)
21 g. protein
8 g. carbohydrates
24 g. fat
64% calories from fat, but...27% from saturated fat*
44 mg. calcium
380 mg. sodium

Grandma's Blueberry Cobbler
...now healthy

Thanks to Ronnie Hoyt
Senior VP, General Merchandise Manager, Wal-Mart

This is a healthy remake of a classic favorite. Many family recipes can be updated with some healthy substitutions and a watchful eye on portions! Keep in mind healthy substitutions when baking — non-fat milk, egg whites, applesauce in place of oil...you'll be amazed at the results!

INGREDIENTS

4 cups	fresh blueberries
1 tsp	lemon juice
	cooking spray
1 cup	all-purpose flour
½ cup	sugar
1 tsp	baking powder
¼ tsp	ground nutmeg
	pinch of salt
1 Tbsp	vegetable oil
½ tsp	vanilla extract
2	large egg whites, lightly beaten
3 Tbsp	sugar
½ tsp	ground cinnamon

PREPARATION

- Preheat oven to 350 degrees.
- Combine blueberries and lemon juice in a baking dish coated with cooking spray, stir.
- Combine flour, sugar, baking powder, nutmeg and salt into bowl, make a well in center. Combine oil, vanilla, and egg whites, stir with a whisk. Add to flour mixture, stirring until moist.
- Drop dough by spoonfuls onto blueberry mixture to form 8 dumplings. Combine 3 tsp sugar and cinnamon and sprinkle over dumplings.
- Bake at 350° for 30 minutes, until filling is bubbly and dumplings are lightly browned.

NUTRITIONAL ANALYSIS
Servings per recipe: 8
Per serving:
182 calories
3 g. protein
39 g. carbohydrates
2 g. fat
10% calories from fat
39 mg. calcium

Chapter 2

Recipe For A Healthy Heart

Let your heart guide you.

It whispers, so listen closely.

from "The Land Before Time"

Our recipe for a healthy heart begins very simply…

Develop a Passion for Taking Care of your Heart

and the rest of your body will reap the rewards, as well.

This may sound simple for such a complicated organ, but the fact is, that what's good for your heart, is also beneficial for the prevention of many other diseases, and vice versa.

We are certainly making progress in educating women about heart disease, yet many people are still not aware that heart disease is the number one killer of women. More women die of heart disease each year than all cancers combined! 37% of the women in America will die from heart disease, and if you combine that with stroke, the number jumps to more than 50%. Many women still perceive breast cancer as their greatest health threat. While it's estimated that one in eight women will get breast cancer at some point during their lifetime, thanks to education and improved diagnostics, breast cancer is now very treatable and curable…fewer than 5% will die from it. We've come a long way in empowering women to take charge of their breast health…now it's time to focus on our hearts with the same passion! The good news is that for many people, heart disease is mostly preventable. The following page gives you a "recipe" for a healthy heart!

Recipe Makeover
A "Recipe" for Heart Health

What are the symptoms of heart attack in women?

Heart attack symptoms in women may be very different from those in men, and they may be far more subtle.

Feeling breathless,
often without chest pain

Flu-like symptoms,
nausea, clamminess, cold sweats

Unexplained fatigue,
weakness or dizziness

Pain,
in the upper back, shoulders, neck or jaw

Feelings of anxiety

If you experience these symptoms, seek medical attention immediately. Don't hesitate to call 911.

✔ Eat a balanced diet, high in fiber, low in fat and rich in variety

✔ Stop smoking (you'll notice the benefits within a few days, and your heart can recover faster than you may realize!)

✔ Maintain a healthy blood pressure, ideally below 120/80

✔ Keep a healthy blood cholesterol level. Talk to your doctor about your ideal HDL/LDL ratio.

✔ Understand your family history and personal risk factors

✔ Enjoy a physically active lifestyle which includes a minimum of 30 minutes of exercise at least 3 days a week

✔ Maintain a healthy weight

✔ Work with your doctor to understand diabetes and control its effect on your heart's health

✔ Know and understand the symptoms of heart attack in women

✔ Talk to your doctor about heart disease and your personal need for screenings and diagnostics

✔ Be aware of how stress affects you and learn how to keep it in check to protect your heart

Friendships: Research shows that women who have strong friendships are less likely to have a second heart attack.

*A*s women, we need to "encourage" the medical community to screen women for heart disease, both in oral histories and in diagnostic screenings. If you have a stress test, either as part of your annual physical, or because of family history or your personal risk factors, ask to have an ECHO stress test. According to Holly Thacker, MD, Director, Cleveland Clinic Foundation Women's Health Center, "many doctors believe this test more accurately recognizes serious heart problems in women."

Many researchers are beginning to look at inflammation as a predictor for heart disease. A simple, inexpensive blood test which measures levels of C-Reactive Protein (CRP) may help your doctor identify your risk. The high level of this protein indicates that inflammation is present, and this may put you at increased risk of coronary artery disease, and…some of the newest thinking has linked a high CRP to an elevated risk of colon cancer. Talk to your doctor for more information.

For years, most of us, and even many in the medical profession, viewed heart disease as a man's disease. Thankfully, we now know better! Studies have concluded that many women may be at an even greater risk for dying of heart disease than their male counterparts. Some reasons may be that women typically wait longer to seek treatment after the onset of symptoms of a heart attack. In addition, many women do not recognize their symptoms as those of a heart attack. We now know that "typical symptoms" may be quite different for a woman than for a man. Your chance of survival may depend of your recognition of these symptoms. See side panel of page 22.

Unfortunately, 63% of women who died suddenly from heart attack had not reported previous symptoms. The good news is that recently we've learned a great deal about the symptoms of heart attack in women, and how a woman's heart may actually predict a heart attack. A November 2003 study published in Circulation, the journal of the American Heart Association, found that the main symptoms women experienced a month prior to having a heart attack were extreme fatigue and an interruption in sleep patterns. The challenge here is that these are typical for many busy, on-the-go women. It's important to recognize the difference between being tired and the type of extreme fatigue that may be your best warning sign of trouble. If climbing a flight of stairs tires you now, but didn't a few weeks ago…it's time to see your doctor! Any change in what is "typical" for you should be reported to your physician. Learn to read your body the way you read a recipe. Look at all the ingredients, see how they fit together, and imagine the successful finished product!

$\mathcal{T}$he Essential Ingredients

You can alter the "recipe"...The best place to start is with awareness.
Know your risk factors and discuss them with your doctor. It's important for
at-risk women to **develop an action plan** with their doctors. There are many things
you can do every day to reduce your risk of developing heart disease and to save your
life. The important thing is that you must make healthy lifestyle changes and stick
with them, every day. That may mean making some changes, but the rewards are
well worth it! These changes don't have to be extreme. In fact, experts say that
starting with small changes like a bit less fat, a few more fruits and veggies, and just
walking 20 minutes a day are some good ways to get started. **You will see results...**
and, you'll be encouraged to make your diet even healthier, and exercise a bit
more...Now, that's a "recipe" for success!

**When you're ready for a more advanced "recipe"...Incorporate 30 minutes
of activity into your day.**
This can even be broken into three 10-minute intervals...park as far away from your
office as possible, or get off the bus a few stops early and walk. Take the stairs instead
of the elevator. Need to send a file to a co-worker in another building...why not
walk?

Take advantage of every opportunity that presents itself to be active! Do a few laps
around the soccer field during your child's practice. Put yourself in the picture of a
physically-active lifestyle and you'll have more energy, look better, and may even
prevent heart disease!

Get passionate about a heart-healthy diet.
Here's how to develop a passion for healthy foods. On the way to your neighborhood
market or grocery store, change the channel...mentally and physically. Turn the car
radio to a fun station – whether you love gospel, rock, nostalgic fifties and sixties, or

peaceful classical music. When you enter the store, have a smile on your face. You should feel very happy, you're about to start a wonderful journey...and at the end of the rainbow (rainbows of vibrant colors, of fresh fruits or veggies, and don't forget that pretty pink salmon), is a healthier lifestyle, a more fit body and a less-stressed mind. When you bring the healthy food into your kitchen, know that you are doing something good, not only for yourself, but for your entire family. When you cook, use fun new recipes (like the ones in this book) or, amend Grandma's to make them healthier. Serve your meal on new dishes or new placemats and...put some fresh flowers on the table. You and your entire family can begin to develop a passion for living well...and you can all have healthy hearts.

Keep an eye on stress!

Some amount of stress is unavoidable. But, recent research suggests that it's the way you react to stress that makes the difference. Research shows that people whose blood pressure spikes during mental stress are six times more likely to have a heart attack or other serious cardiac event within six months than those who have less of a reaction. What's the secret? Tame your tension!

Effective techniques for stress management

Deep Breathing,
in through the nose, out through the mouth...slowly! Focus on the movement of your breath into your lungs and then out through your mouth.

Meditation,
close your eyes and focus on...nothing!

Practice Yoga,
this is a great way to reduce your stress and stretch your body to eliminate toxic chemicals we may harbor when stressed. Don't have time for a full session? Then just take a few minutes at your desk to roll your neck and shoulders around to reduce the tension they're holding.

Spend time with family and friends,
do what you enjoy and are passionate about.

Make time for yourself a must on your to-do list!

Goodness Grapes-ious?

These richly colored globes of tangy sweetness deliver a lot more than flavor...they may help protect your heart. Grapes contain two beneficial flavenoids... proanthocyanin and catechins. These potent antioxidants may enhance cardiovascular health by assisting the body's circulatory system, helping blood vessels maintain their elasticity, and helping reduce cell damage. Each individual grape contains more than 1,000 different flavenoids! Grapes are also a good source of potassium – a nutrient with vital benefits for nerve and heart function.

Develop a passion for eating well!
10 Tips for a heart-healthy diet

1. **Eat your Veggies!** Vegetables contain a wealth of nutrients that can protect your heart. Raw or cooked, it doesn't matter; a good goal is to consume 10 different varieties every week. Try to include generous amounts of dark green, orange and red vegetables.

2. **Choose whole fruits rather than juice.** Fruit has many of the benefits of vegetables, but when you drink only the juice, you're missing out on the fiber. Include fruits with edible skin and seeds at meals and snacks.

3. **Add whole grains to your daily diet.** Make sure half your daily grain intake is the "whole" thing. When buying bread, crackers or cereal, look for "whole wheat," "whole oats," or "whole rye" as the first ingredient. Try brown rice, bulgur, barley and whole wheat pasta.

4. **Got calcium?** Low-fat, that is! Everyone knows that calcium helps keep our bones strong. Now, recent research reveals the essential role of calcium in helping to control both weight and blood pressure. The best place to get calcium is milk and dairy products. But since milk contains animal fat, choose 1% or non-fat, and try for two to three servings daily. Low-fat yogurt, cheese and pudding count, too! If you drink soy milk, buy a brand that is fortified with calcium.

5. **Select lean meats!** You don't have to give up meat, just the fat. Choose meats with the words "loin" or "round" in the name, and limit portions to no more than three ounces cooked weight.

6. **Add fish at least two times per week.** All fish are heart healthy, and some are a very good source of Omega-3 fatty acids, a type of fat especially good for the heart and cardiovascular system. It also may reduce risks of cancer, and may reduce the severity and pain of symptoms of rheumatoid arthritis, Crohn's disease, ulcerative colitis and asthma. Choose from salmon, canned light tuna, herring, shrimp, pollock and catfish.

7. **Limit animal fats and trans fatty acids.** Foods made with hydrogenated fats contain trans fatty acids. Choosing some "good fats", like the Omega-3s found in fish, like those listed above, and those from vegetable or seed oils (like olive, canola or peanut), can help protect against problems with the immune system, hardened arteries, and scaling skin, among other symptoms.

8. **Use legumes (dried beans) as a healthy alternative to meat.** Beans provide needed protein without the fat and cholesterol of meat. An added bonus is their high fiber content.

9. **Moderate your sodium intake.** Too much sodium is associated with high blood pressure, a risk factor for heart disease and stroke. Go easy on adding salt while cooking, or at the table.

10. **Maintain a healthy body weight.** Match your food intake with your energy output. Watch out for larger portions – especially in restaurants – that cause you to eat more than you need. Learn to listen to your body's signals for hunger and fullness.

A word about mercury...

As we've said, both fish and shellfish are an important part of a healthy diet. You've no doubt heard the warnings about mercury in fish. Here's the straight scoop, issued from both the EPA and the FDA:

By following these 3 recommendations for selecting and eating fish or shellfish, women and young children will receive the benefits of eating fish and shellfish and be confident that they have reduced their exposure to the harmful effects of mercury.

1. Do not eat Shark, Swordfish, King Mackerel, or Tilefish because they contain high levels of mercury.

2. Eat up to 12 ounces (2 average meals) a week of a variety of fish and shellfish that are lower in mercury. These include shrimp, canned light tuna, salmon, pollock, and catfish.

Light or albacore? When choosing tuna, bear in mind that albacore ("white") tuna has more mercury than canned light tuna.

3. Check local advisories about the safety of fish caught by family and friends in your local lakes, rivers, and coastal areas. If no advice is available, eat up to 6 ounces (one average meal) per week of fish you catch from local waters, but don't consume any other fish during that week.

You may have one of the biggest risk factors for heart attack, and your doctor may not even know it.

Watch out for depression

While doctors screening for heart problems know to monitor smoking, high cholesterol and high blood pressure, many doctors may miss a more serious foe – **depression**. Numerous studies link depression to increased heart attack risk, by as much as 70%. And, depression may increase the chance of dying in the months following a heart attack by as much as $3\frac{1}{2}$ times.

More evidence about the link between depression and heart attack came recently from the Women's Health Initiative, the largest-ever study of post-menopausal women. Among the more than 93,000 women studied, women who were depressed had a 50% greater chance of dying from cardiovascular disease than women who didn't show signs of depression. The study showed that, even among healthy women with no prior history of heart problems, depression proved to be a significant risk factor for developing, and later dying from, heart disease. Doctors are now trying to determine the best ways to treat depression, and protect our hearts in the process.

Baby Yourself - An aspirin a day

There's been much media attention lately regarding who should and who should not take an aspirin each day to ward off heart attack. And, most-recent studies have even linked daily aspirin therapy to a reduction in breast cancer. Talk to your doctor…but, here's the latest thinking. A recent analysis of 15 years of data found that aspirin does indeed reduce the risk of a first heart attack – by a whopping 32%! These findings support the American Heart Association guidelines recommending a daily aspirin (not acetaminophen). This may not work for everyone, however. For some, the benefits of taking an aspirin a day may not outweigh the risk associated with taking it. A good rule of thumb is that if you are over age 50, and have at least two other serious risk factors for heart disease, talk to your doctor about aspirin therapy.

Be your Berry Best!

Generations have known that cranberries may prevent urinary tract infections. Research now suggests that these bright, colorful berries may also have a positive influence on blood cholesterol and may reduce the severity of brain damage after stroke. Similar studies have also shown that blueberries are one of nature's strongest antioxidant foods, much of which comes from their deep purple-blue color. The secret "ingredient" found in the deep reds of cranberries and the rich purples of blueberries are natural dyes called anthocyanins, which are antioxidants that, as we said on page 15, may help enhance your cardiovascular health and reduce your risk of cancer, arthritis, memory loss and other effects of aging. Several studies have shown that people with diets high in antioxidant-rich fruits and vegetables can substantially increase the amount of antioxidants in their blood. Although strawberries, raspberries and cherries also contain anthocyanins, the level found in blueberries is among the highest of the pigments studied thus far.

Follow Your Heart – A healthy chain of events

Many women visit their gynecologists each year for an exam, but not as many actually see a primary care physician for a whole-body annual physical exam. This is essential to measure the health of the REST of your body…including your heart! If you have significant risk factors for heart disease, your doctor may consider putting you in the care of a heart specialist, or cardiologist. And, within the category of heart disease, many doctors specialize in certain areas, including congestive heart failure, arrhythmia, coronary artery disease or vascular disease.

The Wonder Fruit!

Although no fruit or vegetable provides a complete balance of nutrients, the avocado offers a wonderful assortment. It provides an array of essential vitamins and minerals, including potassium, magnesium, folic acid, thiamin, riboflavin, niacin, biotin, pantothenic acid and Vitamins E & K. Plus, the avocado contains phytonutrients that may help lower blood cholesterol and protect against some cancers. It also has a good amount of protein, and yes…a lot of fat! But…it's primarily mono-unsaturated fat…the good kind! So, dig into the healthy recipe for guacamole on the following page. ENJOY!

Great Guacamole

Thanks to Leslie Barraza
Corporate Marketing Assistant, Wal-Mart

Guacamole is a favorite for any dipping occasion...and, now we know that it's loaded with "Good" fat! See page 29 for more information on the heart-healthy avocado!

INGREDIENTS

3 to 5	ripe avocados, seeded and peeled
⅓ cup	onion, finely chopped
1 clove	garlic, minced
1	tomato, diced (optional)
2 oz.	low-fat cream cheese
3 to 4 drops	hot pepper sauce
¼ cup	fresh cilantro, finely chopped
2 Tbsp	fresh lime juice
	Lawry's seasoned salt, to taste

PREPARATION

- In a large mixing bowl, coarsely mash avocados, leaving some chunks.
- Add remaining ingredients and mix to blend.

Guacamole is best made as close to serving as possible. For short-term storage, seal in an airtight container with a piece of plastic wrap against the surface of the guacamole.

FEELING FESTIVE? Spice up your basic guacamole with these fun suggestions!

California Dreamin'
Substitute goat cheese for cream cheese and toss in some pistachios for a fun California-inspired treat!

Mediterranean Flair
Add 1 tsp ground cumin for a slightly different taste.

¿Que Pasa?
Add diced green chilies to spice up your taste buds.

Parlez vous Français?
Add 1 Tbsp of dry vermouth and a pinch of dried tarragon for a taste of France.

NUTRITIONAL ANALYSIS
Servings per recipe: 10 one-half cup servings
Per serving:
Basic recipe
91 calories
2 g. protein
5 g. carbohydrates
8 g. fat
79% calories from fat, but...only 17% calories from saturated fat...the rest is "good" fat!
15 mg. calcium

Heart Healthy Grilled or Baked Salmon

Thanks to Valerie Simpson
National Minority Spokesperson, Singer/Songwriter

There are plenty of ways to enjoy salmon...this is a simple, quick and easy recipe that tastes great everytime! Consider topping with a salsa from page 131 for an added kick.

INGREDIENTS

3 lbs	salmon fillet
	dried dill
	garlic powder
	small dash of Jane's Crazy Salt or Morton's "No Salt"
1 Tbsp	fat-free mayonnaise
	Optional:
	sprigs of fresh lovage

PREPARATION

- Pre-heat charcoal grill or if using an oven, pre-heat to 450 degrees.
- Lay flat a length of Heavy Duty Aluminum Foil, long enough to extend 5 inches beyond each end of the salmon fillet. Form a "pan" by rolling up all 4 sides of the foil to make the sides of the "pan". Spraying the foil with a non-stick spray will make it easier to slice and serve.
- Sprinkle the salmon with dill, garlic powder, and very lightly with seasoned salt or salt substitute.
- Spread 1 Tbsp fat-free mayo to keep salmon moist while cooking at these high temps.
- If you have fresh lovage, lay it across the salmon.
- If using the oven, cooking time is approx. 15 to 17 minutes, depending on thickness of fish.
- If grilling, it takes from 20 to 30 minutes, depending on thickness of fish and whether or not your grill has a lid. (Using a lid cooks the fish faster.)
- Before cutting and serving the salmon, remove the lovage, if using.

NUTRITIONAL ANALYSIS
Servings per recipe: 8
Each 6 oz. serving contains:
290 calories
37 g. protein
Fewer than 2 g. carbohydrates
15 g. fat
47% calories from fat, but...only 8% calories from saturated fat
18 mg. calcium

Chapter 3

Strong Bones

If you can't get rid of the skeleton in your closet... you'd best teach it to dance.

George Bernard Shaw

Our recipe for strong bones
begins very simply...

Build them

and keep them strong!

everal years ago Speaking of Women's Health launched our continuing educational initiative on osteoporosis. What began as education and awareness to build strong bones, now includes new medicines to actually build bone mass and prevent bone fractures. Osteoporosis is a treatable, and often preventable, disease.

When you're young, your skeleton acts as a calcium bank for the rest of your body, taking in new deposits that help replace old bone. By the time you reach your mid-30s, though, it's easier to lose bone than to gain it. From then on, bones tend to become less dense and more brittle. This can be a "recipe" for disaster.

Osteoporosis is a disease that thins and weakens bones to the point where they break easily — especially bones in the hip, backbone (spine) and wrist. Osteoporosis is called the "silent disease" — you may not notice any changes until a bone breaks. But your bones may have been losing density over many years.

Bones play many roles in the body

Bones provide structure, protect organs, anchor muscles, and store calcium. Bone is living tissue.

To keep bones strong, the body is always breaking down old bone and replacing it with new tissue. As people enter their 40s and 50s, more bone is broken down than is replaced. A close look at the inside of bone would show something that looks like a honeycomb. When you have osteoporosis, the spaces in this honeycomb grow larger. The outer shell of your bones also gets thinner. All this makes your bones weaker.

Osteoporosis is incredibly common. A woman's risk of developing osteoporosis rises with age, especially in the first five to seven years after menopause. During this time, drops in estrogen may result in a 20% loss of bone mass. For women older than 50, the risk of suffering an osteoporosis-related bone fracture at some point is about 50%. Think a broken bone is no big deal? Think again!! Complications from an osteoporosis-related fracture may be so serious as to even lead to death.

But don't panic…the good news is that osteoporosis can be treated at any age. Talk to your doctor about what you can do to prevent bone fractures.

How Do I Know If I Am Losing Bone?

Losing height or having a bone break easily is often the first sign of osteoporosis. But it doesn't need to be. Bone density is a term that describes how solid your bones are. Ordinary x-rays do not show bone loss until a massive amount of bone is gone. The gold standard for measuring bone density is a **DEXA-scan** (*dual-energy x-ray absorptiometry*). The DEXA-scan tells your risk of fracture. It could show that you have normal bone density. Or, it could show that you have osteopenia (decreased density) or even osteoporosis (advanced bone loss). Ask your doctor about this test if you think you are at risk for osteoporosis or if you are a woman around the age of menopause or older.

As we said, it's never too late to start treating osteoporosis – or too early to start preventing it. Osteoporosis is not just an "Old Lady's" disease. Younger women who have had surgical menopause (ovaries removed), or eating disorders, or have taken certain medications may be at increased risk. Be sure to discuss these possibilities with your doctor. **Even if you know you're not at risk right now for osteoporosis, read the next few pages anyway.** It will arm you with life-saving information for later in your life as well as give you some nutritional information that may help you prevent osteoporosis! This also gives you an opportunity to be an "agent of change" for women in your life who, unfortunately, have already developed osteoporosis. The next few pages will give you the good news about treating osteoporosis, building back lost bone and preventing fractures. It is also a great opportunity to begin a dialogue with your mother, aunts and grandmothers about health risks and family history. In the same way that you would ask your doctor a variety of questions, ask your family members about lifestyle and medical history. You will want to know if anyone in your family has suffered from osteoporosis or if they have fractured bones. This information, along with a DEXA-scan will help you:

✔ Detect osteoporosis before a fracture occurs.
✔ Predict your chances of fracturing in the future.
✔ Determine your rate of bone loss and/or monitor the effects of treatment if the test is conducted at intervals of a year or more.

How Is Osteoporosis Treated?

Prevention and treatment of osteoporosis aims to stop bone loss and rebuild bone to prevent fractures. Along with making lifestyle changes, there are several medication choices. Some will slow your rate of bone loss, and others can help rebuild bone. THE GOAL is to avoid fractures.

Adequate calcium, vitamin D, appropriate exercise and, in some cases, medication are important for maintaining bone health. Currently, bisphosphonates [risedronate (Actonel®) and alendronate (Fosamax®)], calcitonin, estrogens, parathyroid hormone and raloxifene (Evista®) are approved by the US Food & Drug Administration (FDA) for the prevention and/or treatment of osteoporosis.

Just as women pass treasured cooking recipes down from generation to generation, it is equally important to pass on information about health risks and family history.

Bisphosphonates make up one group, and they include drugs such as alendronate and risedronate. These drugs have been shown to either reduce or slow bone loss, increase bone density and help reduce fracture risk.

Other types include polypeptides, prescription estrogen or hormone replacement therapy and selective estrogen receptor modulators. A new class of drug, called parathyroid hormone (PTH), such as teriparatide (Forteo®), is now FDA-approved for the treatment of osteoporosis in post-menopausal women and men who are at high risk for a fracture. This medication works to stimulate new bone formation and to increase bone density.

Not all drugs are equal or offer the same benefits. Ask your doctor which will work best for you and help reduce your risk of bone fracture, particularly hip and spine, fastest. As with all prescription drugs, talk with your doctor about benefits, risks and possible side effects.

What About Falls?
For many women, the real devastation of osteoporosis occurs when they slip, fall or trip and fracture a bone – usually the hip or an arm or leg bone. The problems are amplified among older women, who may take longer to recover or never fully walk again after a broken hip.

"When a woman has a hip fracture, a woman's death rate is very high," notes Lana Holstein, MD, "because a fracture like that is a trauma that sets up a reaction throughout the body." Older people who are hospitalized with hip fractures may also be at a higher risk to develop life-threatening pneumonia. Osteoporosis is the cause of 1.5 million fractures each year. **It is important to prevent falls. Put some passion behind this "recipe" for preventing falls....**

✔ Make sure you can see and hear well. Use your glasses or a hearing aid if needed.
✔ Ask your doctor if any of the drugs you are taking can make you dizzy or unsteady on your feet.
✔ Use a cane or walker if your walking is unsteady.
✔ Wear rubber-soled and low-heeled shoes.
✔ Make sure all the rugs and carpeting in your house are firmly attached to the floor, or remove them.
✔ Use bathroom aids, including grab bars and stools, to help steady or pull yourself up. In and out of the tub or shower, use bathmats with rubber backing.
✔ Keep your rooms well lit and the floor free of clutter. Use nightlights.

Osteoporosis has not been as well studied in men as in women. Most prevention and treatment recommendations are based on studies in women. However, many of the risk factors for men are the same as those for women — smoking, not enough calcium or vitamin D, too much alcohol, family history, too little exercise, and taking certain drugs. Low levels of testosterone in older men may increase their loss of bone and chance of hip fracture. Talk to the men in your life (brothers, husband, sons, fathers) about getting the proper medical tests.

The Main Ingredient – Calcium

Whether you're building strong bones to avoid osteoporosis, or treating a diagnosis of osteoporosis, you must have calcium in your diet. Calcium is a mineral needed by the body for healthy bones, teeth, and proper function of the heart, muscles and nerves. Studies have also shown that calcium may also help lower high blood pressure and control weight. The body cannot produce calcium; therefore, it must be absorbed through food. Your body can only absorb calcium in small quantities, and the rest is secreted as waste. For this reason, it's important to include calcium-rich foods with every meal, or by taking small-dosage supplements throughout the day.

How much calcium do you need?

Although our need for calcium changes with age, unfortunately, most Americans get less than half of their calcium needs every day.

AGE	CALCIUM PER DAY	VITAMIN D PER DAY
9-18	1300 mg	
19-50 (premenopausal)	1000 mg	400-800 IU
51 and older	1200 mg	every day
According to the National Osteoporosis Foundation		

Speaking to Men about Health™

What About Osteoporosis in Men? Osteoporosis is not just a woman's disease. Men have it also, although not as often as women do. This may be because most men start with more bone mass than women and lose it more slowly as they age.

According to Speaking of Women's Health speaker and friend, Lana Holstein, MD, "It is very difficult to get enough calcium through your diet alone."

- Each glass of milk has about 300 mg. So, you'd need to drink 4 to 5 glasses each day.
- A cup of broccoli has 172 mg. That's about 8 cups every day!
- And, as much as you may love frozen yogurt, at 80 mg. per cup, you'd need to consume gallons!

"Since it is unlikely that anyone will actually eat 8 cups of broccoli a day," notes Dr. Holstein, "most people will have to add supplements to their dietary sources to get to the recommended daily dosage." (See chart on page 39.) Remember: your body can only absorb calcium in small quantities, and the rest is secreted as waste. For this reason, it's important to include calcium-rich foods with every meal, or to take small dosage-supplements throughout the day.

Sun & Vitamin D

Vitamin D is needed to help your body absorb calcium. Every time you step into the sun, your body produces Vitamin D. This vital mineral is also found in fish oil, egg yolks and fortified milk. If you don't get much sun, you may want to consider taking a Vitamin D supplement to ensure that your body gets the value of 400 to 800 IU of Vitamin D daily. Even if you are conscientious and wear sun protection of at least SPF 15, it may be impossible to take in enough sun to absorb the calcium in your diet. Be sure that your calcium supplement includes Vitamin D.

Exercise... Another ingredient in a "recipe" for healthy bones.

Evidence shows that inactivity leads to loss of bone mass. Regular weight-bearing exercise (i.e., walking, running and dancing) and regular strength training exercise (i.e., free weights, machine weights and elastic bands) increase bone mass or bone strength. We call this weight-bearing exercise because your body bears your own weight.

- **Exercise needs to be site-specific.** For example, walking regularly increases bone mass in the hip and lower back but not wrist bone mass. And...while swimming and bicycle riding are great cardiovascular exercises, they are not weight-bearing exercises, and will not help you build strong bones. The reason these are not considered weight-bearing is that the water and the bicycle are bearing your weight.
- **Regular exercise helps increase balance and coordination and reduces the risk of falls and subsequent fractures.** Posture exercises can help prevent or reduce the slumping posture often associated with osteoporosis.

Recipe Makeover
Better Bones

Calcium-rich foods

- ✔ Dairy foods such as milk, cheese, yogurt and ice cream
- ✔ Calcium-added orange juice and other juices
- ✔ Calcium-added cereals, breakfast bars and breads
- ✔ Mozzarella, ricotta, cheddar, Swiss, cottage and parmesan cheeses
- ✔ Canned salmon with bones and sardines
- ✔ Navy beans
- ✔ Nuts
- ✔ Tofu
- ✔ Turnips, kale, broccoli, leafy green vegetables
- ✔ Blackstrap molasses

The foods listed above help us gain calcium. Be sure to see our recipe for Mac & Cheese at the end of this chapter.

Calcium-depleting foods
Some other foods and activities may actually rob us of calcium. Be sure to use the following in moderation.

- To protect your stores of calcium, you may want to limit your intake of salt, sodium or salty foods. Choose low sodium prepared foods, when possible.
- Researchers recommend that you limit your intake of caffeinated beverages to one or two servings daily.
- Although early research suggested that a high protein diet might interfere with your body's ability to absorb calcium, recent studies show the opposite. Now it's believed that a high protein diet may actually help build strong bones.
- Some commonly used medicines can cause loss of bone mass. These include glucocorticoids (a type of steroids) which are used to control diseases such as arthritis and asthma, some antiseizure drugs, certain sleeping pills, some hormones that treat endometriosis, and some cancer drugs. An overactive thyroid gland or using too much thyroid hormone for an underactive thyroid can also be a problem. If you are taking these medicines, talk to your doctor about what can be done to protect your bones.
- Excessive alcohol intake also inhibits the body's ability to absorb calcium.
- Women who smoke have lower levels of estrogen, which weakens bones. In addition, nicotine inhibits the body's ability to absorb calcium…so, even with an adequate diet and supplements, you may not absorb enough calcium to build strong bones.

Mac & Cheese

Thanks to Pat Curran
Senior VP, Division U Operations, Wal-Mart

This recipe is the All-American comfort food. Prepare this as a side dish, or if using as a main dish, add some veggies...see healthy additions below.

INGREDIENTS

1 Tbsp	butter
1/4 cup	all purpose flour
1 cup	fat-free milk
1/4 cup	fat-free sour cream
1 tsp	dry mustard
	salt and pepper to taste
4 oz. each	low-fat cheddar, jack and sharp cheddar cheeses
16 oz. pkg.	of pasta – elbow, fussilli, rigatoni, pick your favorite!

If serving as a side dish, limit portion size to one-half to three-quarters of a cup. This equals fewer calories and just as much flavor!

PREPARATION

- Preheat oven to 350 degrees.
- Boil pasta according to package directions, omitting salt and fat.
- In separate saucepan, melt butter. Add flour and stir together. Slowly add milk, stirring constantly to form a roux. Adding milk too quickly will cause roux to be lumpy.
- Reserve about 2 oz. cheese. Add the rest to the sauce, along with mustard, sour cream, and salt and pepper. Stir until cheese is melted and sauce is smooth.
- Combine sauce with cooked noodles and pour into casserole or baking dish. Sprinkle remaining cheese on top. Bake uncovered at 350° for 20 minutes.

Healthy Additions
Consider adding frozen peas or chopped broccoli to this dish just before baking....it's colorful, adds veggies and is a healthy way to make the portion larger...and you can have one of your daily servings of vegetables!

NUTRITIONAL ANALYSIS
Servings per recipe: 8
Each 1-cup (about the size of a fist) **serving contains:**
371 calories
21 g. protein
49 g. carbohydrates
9 g. fat
22% calories from fat
311 mg. calcium

Lentil Soup

Thanks to Steven Cawood
Corporate Marketing Manager, Wal-Mart

This hearty soup is chock full of veggies and tastes great! Warm up on a cool night with this healthy favorite! Serve with warm cornbread or your favorite "whole grain" bread.

INGREDIENTS

1	onion, chopped
¼ cup	olive oil
2	carrots, diced
2	stalks celery, chopped
2	cloves garlic, minced
1 tsp	dried oregano
1	bay leaf
1 tsp	dried basil
1 (14.5 oz.) can	crushed tomatoes
2 cups	dry lentils
8 cups	water
½ cup	spinach, rinsed and thinly sliced
2 Tbsp	vinegar
	salt to taste
	ground black pepper to taste

PREPARATION

- In a large soup pot, heat oil over medium heat. Add onions, carrots, and celery; cook and stir until onion is tender.
- Stir in garlic, bay leaf, oregano, and basil; cook for 2 minutes.
- Stir in lentils, and add water and tomatoes. Bring to a boil. Reduce heat, and simmer for at least 1 hour.
- When ready to serve stir in spinach, and cook until it wilts.
- Stir in vinegar, and season to taste with salt and pepper, and more vinegar if desired.

Top it Off!

Add a dollop of low-fat cheese or sour cream just before serving.

NUTRITIONAL ANALYSIS
Servings per recipe: 6-8
Servings size: approximately 1 cup
Per serving:
327 calories
19 g. protein
44 g. carbohydrates (22 g. dietary fiber)
10 g. fat
28% calories from fat
74 mg. calcium

Chapter 4

I still find each day too short for all the thoughts I want to think, all the walks I want to take, all the books I want to read, and all the friends I want to see.

John Burroughs

Our recipe for energy and vitality begins very simply …

Be Active!

Maintain a physically-active lifestyle and your body will look more fit and fabulous.

Exercise is extremely important throughout a woman's lifetime and particularly as she gets older. There's no question that physical activity promotes health and helps reduce your risk for many diseases. The benefits include a lower risk of heart disease and obesity; healthy bones, muscles and joints; more lean muscle and lower body fat; and increased mental activity. Research has shown that exercise increases the brain's alpha waves — patterns of electrical activity, associated with relaxation. Vigorous exercise may decrease muscle tension while simultaneously increasing your heart rate, which helps you stay alert. Physical activity reduces the risk of diabetes and colon cancer, and helps lower high blood pressure. Physical activity can help improve your mood and confidence. It can also reduce the symptoms of anxiety and depression. So clearly, physical activity is the "main ingredient" in a "recipe" for "dishing up" a body that is physically and mentally fit.

And, there's more good news! Recent estimates show that 40% of women in America do engage in some type of regular physical activity. If you're among them…keep up the good work! You're keeping your heart and body in good shape!

With all this good news...Women who are not regularly active need to GET MOVING!

If you exercise for about 30 minutes most days, you could:

Lower your cholesterol and blood pressure levels

Improve your sleep

Increase oxygen to the brain and improve memory

Make your bones stronger and improve posture

Burn stored body fat to help you lose weight

Reduce stress and tension

Increase energy

Protect your body from injury and disease

Slow the aging process

Boost self-confidence

How much exercise do you really need?

You don't have to "train" to achieve some healthy benefits from activity. A smaller amount of physical activity than you might think, may help you stay healthy. To improve overall health, you need to have some type of physical activity for 30 minutes, for a minimum of three days each week. This does not have to be an activity for 30 minutes in a row. You can be active for 10 minutes at a time, three times a day. If your goal is to lose weight, you might have to increase your activity more. *It is best to talk with your health care provider before you start an exercise program or if you want to lose weight.* All this according to Ronda Gates, MS RPh. In addition to being a registered pharmacist, Ronda Gates is a Fitness and Health Promotion Specialist.

What counts?

According to the US Surgeon General's office, a "moderate amount of physical activity" means burning about 150 calories a day, or about 1,000 calories a week. Plainly put, exercise means activity. It means movement. It means doing something physical that gets your heart pumping and makes you break into a sweat. If your body is doing any of these, you're exercising! (*Remember, before automobiles, television, modern appliances, elevators and computers, human beings moved around a LOT every single day*). Activities such as walking, gardening, climbing stairs, bicycling, swimming and jogging can improve a woman's overall health. For beginners, 5 to 10 minutes of activity a few times a week is a good starting point. You can then work up to the recommended physical activity level for your age and fitness level.

Three types of exercise
A complete fitness program includes three components, according to the American Council on Exercise.

Aerobic exercise is any activity that uses large muscle groups in a continuous, rhythmic fashion for sustained periods of time, enough to get the heart and lungs working and pumping. Need some examples? Running and jogging in place is considered aerobic activity. A fast-paced fitness or dance class is aerobic. Dancing, playing volleyball, swimming...any activity that keeps the heart and lungs working consistently is considered aerobic, because the activity pumps oxygenated blood throughout your body.

Muscular strength and endurance conditioning includes the use of free weights or weight-lifting machines that challenge all major muscle groups – arms, chest, back, stomach, hips and legs. These types of weight-bearing exercises are especially important for maintaining the health and density of your bones, and for women, healthy bones mean you're preventing the development of osteoporosis. And of course, don't forget the most basic "ingredient" for weight-bearing exercise...walking! Walking is considered weight-bearing because your body is bearing your own weight. Put on that pedometer, and start counting your steps to stronger bones. (See page 52.)

Where the rubber meets the muscle

Many experts recommend using stretch bands or exercise bands for resistance as an alternative to weights. These are lightweight, portable wide bands which distribute resistive force evenly, helping to build muscle strength, which may help reduce your chance of injury. Bands have been used by physical and occupational therapists for years and have recently grown in popularity among everyday women just like all of us. These stretch bands are easy to use at home and take up no room in your suitcase.

Keep Moving!

Many women tell us that, despite the best of intentions and multiple efforts, they just cannot seem to stick with an exercise program. This chapter includes some proven strategies to help make fitness a way of life.

A strength or conditioning program doesn't require a set of dumbbells in the basement. You can use some simple hand weights or heavy items found around the house – a smooth rock, even a can of soup or jugs of laundry detergent with handles. Go through a simple routine of lifting them over your head and/or out to your side, while you do some standing squats. Take a walk and strap some ankle weights on before you head out. Sit-ups, push-ups, deep knee bends and yoga stretches are all considered strength and weight-bearing exercises.

Flexibility means stretching that involves all major muscle groups. Before and after each workout, make sure that you stretch well and hold a mild stretch 10 to 30 seconds. Start simply. Bend at the waist and let your arms drape toward the floor. Hold the pose for 20 to 30 seconds, bending a little lower with each deep breath. Do standing stretches, making sure to reach arms and hands outward and upward for prolonged poses, and be sure to hold it at least 10 seconds. As with strength conditioning, try to stretch all major muscle groups and areas of the body.

Really FEEL the muscles and underlying tissue loosen up and stretch out as you try different poses and techniques. A simple stretching or yoga book will help you get started.

A "menu plan" for success

Once you're convinced that exercise can be fun and easy, draw up a contract with yourself outlining realistic daily and weekly goals. Put exercise on your calendar just as you would any other appointment. It may help to enlist a partner or friend to offer encouragement and support, and to help keep you honest. The next time a friend invites you to get together, suggest a workout. Need to meet with a co-worker to discuss an upcoming project? How about a lunchtime walk instead of an in-office meeting? You can jot down a few notes and recap via e-mail when you return to your desk. Here's a new idea for a "recipe exchange": one week you choose the workout activity and the next week, your friend chooses.

Make the most of the time you already have. Instead of trying to find more and more time to exercise, use the time you already have set aside for "other" things! Do your kids have soccer practice? Swim lessons? Combine your workout with another scheduled commitment — walk or run around the park during your kids' soccer or baseball practice, hit the treadmill or cardio machine at "the gym" while your kids have tennis or swim lessons. Get organized. If you have lunches to pack, or kids' clothes to set out for the next day...think of yourself, too! This might mean pre-packing a gym bag for the next day, setting your exercise attire out the night before or keeping extra batteries for your portable CD player.

"Slow-cooking recipes" are delicious, too!

After a month, your body will become more efficient at using blood and oxygen, adding to your endurance. Don't expect an overnight sensation or "extreme" change...a leaner body or slow and steady weight loss may take several months to notice. Relax. It will happen if you keep moving!

A Varied Exercise "Menu"

Pick whatever activity or variety of activities you prefer. The most important thing is...you must enjoy it! When it gets boring...switch to something new. If you cannot bear the heat, try swimming or exercise in an air-conditioned space during the summer. If you love water, but aren't a great swimmer, enroll in a water aerobics class near your home or office. See our exercise "recipes" on the following pages.

A Beginner's "Recipe" with Optional "Ingredients"

A simple definition of exercise:

Activity has three elements — *duration (how many minutes do you exercise?),* **intensity** *(how hard do you work at it?)* and **frequency** *(how often do you do it?)*

By that definition, here's what moderate exercise/activity could involve:

- ✔ **Washing and waxing a car or washing windows/floors for 45-60 minutes**
- ✔ **Playing volleyball for 45 minutes**
- ✔ **Gardening for 30-45 minutes**
- ✔ **Wheeling yourself in a wheelchair for 30-40 minutes**
- ✔ **Walking 1.75 miles in 35 minutes**
- ✔ **Bicycling 5 miles in 30 minutes**
- ✔ **Dancing fast or raking leaves for 30 minutes**
- ✔ **Doing water aerobics for 30 minutes**
- ✔ **Pushing a stroller 1.5 miles in 30 minutes**
- ✔ **Running 1.5 miles in 15 minutes**
- ✔ **Stair-walking for 15 minutes**

See? You do many of these things already. And there are many more options – inline skating, mall walking, softball, water workouts, swimming, ballroom dancing, basketball and jumping rope. Consider purchasing a pedometer to wear all day, every day, to count the number of steps you take. You may be surprised to find that your regular daily activity is near the recommended goal of 10,000 steps per day. Also, studies prove that wearing a pedometer helps encourage you to be more aware of your activity, and helps you step up your activity levels!

"Recipe" for an Ideal Workout

Warm-up (5 – 10 minutes)
Begin with slow walking and gradually increase your pace and resistance (if appropriate).

Aerobic activity (20 – 30 minutes)
This activity should raise your heart rate, and sustain it for a period of 20 minutes (as a goal). **Ask your doctor or a trainer what is the appropriate duration for you.**

Cool down (5 – 10 minutes)
Repeat your warm-up, but in reverse, going from fast to slow.

Strength training
This involves using some weight (a dumbbell, can of soup or flat rock) **to provide resistance. Do 8 – 12 repetitions of several exercises, two to three times each week.**

Walking, the universal "ingredient"
Here's one way to strengthen your heart, your bones and your muscles all in one activity…kind of like a casserole…all the "ingredients" for a healthy workout are included in one dish, or activity, in this case!

Stretching
End each workout this way. Hold your stretch for 10 – 30 seconds. Breathe and relax!

*Exercise with a group
for social interaction
and support*

*Exercise to your
favorite music*

*Keep a written record
of your progress*

*Set realistic goals
for yourself*

*Reward yourself
for progress made…
with something other
than food!*

Your "just" desserts

Your goal may be as simple as walking 5 times your first week, or adding one extra gym workout for 3 weeks in a row. When you achieve your goal, treat yourself to a reward. Consider a new workout outfit or a fresh hair color, or even a pedicure or a massage. And, remember…you will find nothing motivates like success. So it will be easier for you to get back out there and keep moving! Set your next goal and decide what your reward for achieving that will be! Put yourself in the picture of a healthier, more energetic you!

Water, water, water!

Even with moderate activity, dehydration is a major cause of fatigue, poor performance, decreased coordination and muscle cramping. Proper hydration is extremely important before, during and after exercise. The longer and more intensely you exercise, the more important it is to drink plenty of fluids. Inadequate water consumption can be physically harmful. Consider that a loss of as little as 2% of one's body weight due to sweating can lead to a drop in blood volume. When this occurs, the heart works harder in order to move blood through the bloodstream. *Pre*-hydration and *re*-hydration are vital to maintaining cardiovascular health, proper body temperature and muscle function.

LET'S DRINK TO THAT!

The American College of Sports Medicine suggests the following...

✔ **Drink 17 oz.** (2+ cups) **of fluid 2 hours before exercise.**

✔ **Drink every 15 minutes during exercise.**

✔ **Keep drinks cooler than air temperature & close at hand** (a water bottle is ideal).

✔ **If you exercise for more than 60 minutes, you may benefit from a sports drink containing carbohydrates** (not greater than 8% concentration, though).

Although athletes are more prone to suffer symptoms of dehydration, anyone can increase performance & delay fatigue or muscle pain by staying properly hydrated.

Fitness to-go!

If you travel often for work or pleasure, here are some tips to maintain your activity on the road.

Take advantage of hotel fitness facilities to try new machines or add a new element to your usual workout. You might get to try an elliptical machine or stair climber in place of your usual treadmill time. New environments and altitudes can make a dramatic difference. Remember to go easy on the intensity. DON'T OVERDO IT!

Take advantage of the climate you're in (swimming, golfing, skiing, bicycling, hiking).

Be creative and flexible – use the stairs instead of the elevator.

Walk at a nearby mall if weather or safety concerns don't permit outside walking.

Use your exercise bands...they're lightweight and easy to stash in your luggage.

Dressed for success...Comfort is the key!

Dress appropriately. Wear lightweight clothing that breathes and allows sweat to evaporate. Cotton may not be your best choice, because it absorbs perspiration instead of allowing it to move away from the body easily (same goes for socks). Affordable exercise gear can be found almost anywhere. Look for combination fabrics made specifically for exercise. Blended fabrics that allow perspiration to "wick away" from the body are a great choice. The bottom line is, do it your way, you need to feel comfortable and your clothing should not restrict movement in any way.

In winter, dress in layers so that you can remove some layers as your body heats up but put them back on when you cool down. Wear a supportive bra to avoid breast discomfort or premature aging.

If the shoe fits....

Wear good shoes! Good shoes, appropriate for the sport or activity, can make a world of difference in the results. Ill-fitting shoes can cause foot, leg, knee and hip pain, especially if they're worn out or don't have the kind of support that you need for your body type or the particular activity you're doing.

- Try on shoes after a workout at the end of the day, when blood has been circulating and pooling and your feet are the largest.
- Wear the same type of sock that you intend to wear for the sport or activity you have in mind. Always try on BOTH shoes; many people have different-sized or different-shaped feet.
- Forget about a "break-in" period. Shoes should be comfortable the minute you try them on. If not, keep looking!
- The heel should fit firmly with no slipping and you should be able to wiggle all of your toes freely.

A "Recipe" for a Healthy Active Lifestyle

✔ At the store, avoid parking closest to the door. In all cases, think safety first!

✔ Take the stairs!

✔ Use push mowers, brooms and hand trimmers, in addition to powered tools.

✔ If you sit at a desk every day for work, get up and walk around for at least five minutes every hour.

Make your activity fun, so you'll want to do it again. Next time, instead of chatting on the phone with your friend for 30 minutes, arrange to meet for a brisk walk.

Walking to your food will burn calories before you even take the first bite. Plan a picnic that begins with a hike. For a picnic in the park, or even your back yard, try our recipe for BLT Salad. If you're lucky enough to live near the beach, how about a beach party featuring our recipe for Shrimp Pasta.

Gourmet BLT Salad

Thanks to Jill Buhler
Executive Administrative Assistant, Guidant Corporation

This is a healthy "take" on the classic summertime favorite BLT sandwich. It makes a perfect picnic lunch or light dinner.

INGREDIENTS

Dressing

⅓ cup	olive oil
3 Tbsp	lemon juice
2-3 cloves	garlic, minced
	salt and pepper to taste

Salad Fixings

	Romaine lettuce, chopped
	spinach leaves
1	tomato (*sliced or chopped*) (*10 grape or cherry tomatoes sliced in half*)
½ cup	chopped red pepper
½ cup	chopped green onions
2 Tbsp	shredded Swiss cheese
2 Tbsp	shredded Parmesan cheese
2 Tbsp	bacon (*torn into pieces*)
¼ cup	toasted slivered almonds

***Start toasting the almonds first.**
(toasting takes about 10 minutes)

PREPARATIONS

Toasted Slivered Almonds

- Preheat oven to 300 degrees.
- Spray a cookie sheet lightly with olive oil cooking spray and spread the almonds out on the cookie sheet.
- Bake in oven at 300° for 8-10 minutes, or until lightly brown.

Dressing

- Mix together oil, lemon juice, garlic cloves, salt and pepper. Set aside, let sit for at least one-half hour.
- Stir dressing before pouring on to salad.
- Right before serving, pour some dressing over Romaine lettuce and spinach leaves in bowl, toss the lettuce and leaves.
- Add the shredded cheeses, bacon, tomato, red pepper, green onions and toasted almonds over lettuce and toss lightly.

Note: The dressing recipe is enough for two large salads. Do not use the entire recipe on one salad. You can store the dressing in the fridge, for up to 3-4 days. (When using next day, take out of fridge and let dressing "warm up" a bit on counter for 10 minutes, stir and pour.)

FYI – You may also add chopped chicken to this salad to make it a main entrée.

NUTRITIONAL ANALYSIS
Servings per recipe: 4, approximately 1 cup servings
273 calories
8 g. protein
11 g. carbohydrates
24 g. fat
79% calories from fat, but...only 14% from saturated fat.
120 mg. calcium
3.5 g. dietary fiber
*If adding chicken, nutritional analysis will change.

Pasta with Shrimp

Thanks to Scott Berger
Director, Customer Marketing, Wal-Mart Team
Pfizer, Inc.

Serving shrimp always adds a sense of elegance to a meal, whether it's for family or a dinner party. An added bonus is...shrimp is high in protein, low in calories and is available at grocery stores and neighborhood markets.

INGREDIENTS

1½ Tbsp	garlic, chopped
1	medium onion, chopped
2 Tbsp	olive oil
8 oz. can	Italian whole plum tomatoes
1 lb.	cooked shelled shrimp (*can substitute cooked boneless chicken breast*)
1 tsp	oregano
1 tsp	basil
8 oz.	crumbled feta cheese (*optional*)
½ lb. box	linguini
	salt & pepper to taste

PREPARATION

- Boil salted water for the linguini, cooked as directed on the package.
- Sauté chopped garlic and onion in olive oil until tender in a large frying pan 3-5 minutes on medium-high heat.
- Add cooked shrimp, sauté for 2 minutes and remove from pan. Try to keep as much garlic and onion in the pan when removing the shrimp.
- Add the entire can of tomatoes with liquid, stir in the pan.
- Cook until it begins to boil, then reduce heat. Add shrimp, oregano, basil and salt & pepper. Simmer for 3-5 minutes.
- Pour sauce on drained linguini and toss.
- Add crumbled feta cheese, if desired at the table.

NUTRITIONAL ANALYSIS without feta cheese
Serves: 8
Each serving contains approximately:
420 calories
32 g. protein
48 g. carbohydrates
12 g. fat
26% calories from fat
114 mg. calcium
Note: If adding feta, total calories will increase, along with total fat and sodium. Use sparingly, or look for fat-free feta.

Chapter 5

Mental Health

Out of clutter, find simplicity. From discord, find harmony. In the middle of difficulty, lies opportunity.

Albert Einstein

*Our recipe for living well
begins very simply…*

Put Passion Into The Simplest Pleasures…

The feeling of a cool fresh breeze on your face, the smell of fresh sheets on your bed, the sight of a new baby being carried by its mother, sinking into a warm bubble bath while soft music is playing and candlelight is dancing around the tub…these are the simple pleasures, and there's nothing extreme about any of them. But…with a bit of thought and a moment's pause, they can become experiences that fill your heart with joy. Developing an attitude that allows you to have a "Passion" for these simple moments, can also help prepare you for dealing with very serious, even extreme, difficulties that may come into your life. A small adjustment in attitude can make a big difference in how you view the world. Instead of dreading the Saturday errands, enjoy the routine-breaking moments you'll spend; instead of bemoaning your commute, take the opportunity to increase your memory skills by varying your route, listening to a different radio station, rolling your window down and noticing the outside aromas. According to Laurence Katz, PhD, Professor of Neurobiology at Duke University Medical Center, adults can improve their ability to learn new skills and increase their memory by breaking their routine. This sounds so simple, but there is sound research to back this up. When you force your brain to learn something new, it actually builds connectors called *synapses*. These synapses

"It's how we choose to embrace our lives that can take us from just living...to living well."

store memory. Now, you may be wondering why we are talking about memory in a chapter on mental health. Think about it….stress is a huge factor in our mental health, and worrying about "losing" our memory may be a cause for stress. Couple that with a "blah" life that has no "passion" in it and you have a potential for short-term depression. Of course, there are also more serious mental health conditions which, with the help of physicians and counselors, can be dealt with. New medications and therapies are changing the face of dealing with serious depression, schizophrenia and bipolar disease. Later in this chapter, we will define these mental health diseases. For now, let's talk about some of the ways in which you can choose to de-stress.

We have to understand our emotions and *no* professional would ever suggest *never* allowing yourself to feel anger or sadness. Many therapists suggest that you should allow yourself to feel the anger or sadness, then let it go, then balance it by spending a moment thinking of something that brings you joy. Negative emotions, such as anger and anxiety, can weaken the immune system and leave you vulnerable to illness. Stress and tension also increase the risk of high blood pressure, heart disease and dozens of serious complications.

When most women get overwhelmed and overly busy, they first cut back on sleep, exercise and healthy eating. This is an option that will leave you feeling more overwhelmed and less successful! And, it isn't a good idea long term, either.

Feeling stressed or anxious? Chronic stress can have serious health consequences. Fortunately, an antidote is as close as your next breath. Inhale slowly, pause…then, exhale. Conscious breathing is a simple, yet powerful, technique for releasing tension and stress, and for connecting the body, mind and spirit. Just a few minutes of deep breathing each day can help bring you to a state of relaxation.

List your time transitions throughout the day. Many agree that these are often the most challenging points within the day to maintain your calm. Being aware of these "hot" points can help you prepare yourself emotionally, and sometimes, physically, to manage them. Who isn't guilty of running out the office door ten minutes late, fighting traffic while returning calls on your cell phone and running into daycare frazzled, only to pick up a child who feeds off your negative emotions and within a few minutes is deep into a "meltdown"? We've all been there. Now, let's review a new approach…

…it's 5:15. Take a moment to put your desk in order. Think about what you'll need to take home with you and gather it. Now, before you leave your office, take a moment to relax. Close your eyes. Breathe deeply. Roll your head around to release tension from your neck and shoulders. Think of how you'd like your evening to unfold. Think joyfully. Now, for the commute…remember…you can only control your reaction to the situation. Relax. Breathe. When you arrive to pick up your child, put a smile on your face. Turn off your phone. Your child would love to have your attention now. Be prepared with a healthy snack or treat, or just put on your child's favorite song while you drive home. Now into the house to face – the pets, the mail, dinner, homework…RELAX. Take a moment to greet your spouse and children. The mail will still be there later. Change into comfortable clothing if you'd like. Congratulate yourself for maintaining balance up to this point.

Experts agree that when you try to cram too much into too little time, or do too many tasks at once, many fall short on several counts. Perhaps the greatest effect comes to your own sense of well-being. Relax and do each thing you must do, but do it sensibly and with proper perspective. Instead of reading the mail while helping the kids with their homework while you're starting dinner and feeding the pets…take it one thing at a time. Spend a moment with each child to discuss his or her assignments. This is a good opportunity to ask how their day went, and what's on their slate for the next day. By making them your priority, even if just for a few moments, you let them know that you value them and respect their time.

A "Recipe" for Positive Mental Health

✔ Balance is a concept that can benefit every aspect of your life, especially your health. Work must be balanced with play...exercise with rest. On a nutritional level, balance means nourishing yourself with the right nutrients in the right amounts from a variety of foods to keep your body at its healthiest. When you apply the idea of balance consciously and deliberately as you go through each day, it helps you face life's challenges with flexibility, energy and optimism.

✔ Keep a list of positives in your journal or notebook and keep it with you throughout the day. Write yourself notes when you feel joy and positive emotions. When you achieve a goal and feel "on top of the world" write it down, so you can recall this emotion when you need to balance a "low self-esteem" moment.

✔ Take time throughout the day to "recharge" your emotional and physical batteries. As women, we often get so caught up in the business of the day that we forget to take time for ourselves. This may leave you feeling depleted and run down. Take a few moments out of your day to focus on you. It may feel like an indulgence, but it's not! It's as important to good health as eating a nutritious diet or getting a good night's sleep.

More than just a bad hair day?

While we all feel sad or discouraged from time to time, and we all have days when nothing seems to go right….for most of us, as time passes, we work through the problems and our moods begin to brighten. We all get "the blues" now and again, and this is not a particular cause for concern. BUT...if these feelings persist for more than two weeks or begin to interfere with daily activities, it may be depression. **And, depression is an entirely different matter.**

By most estimates, depression – one of the most common forms of mental disorders – affects 20% of women. It's not clear why, but women are twice as likely as men to suffer from depression. **Signs of depression include losing interest in daily activities, diminished appetite, difficulty concentrating, changes in sleep patterns and feelings of guilt and worthlessness.**

Whatever the reason, depression is a real condition and it is treatable in a variety of ways. It can be caused by chemical imbalances and triggered by life changes, and people with a family history are at greater risk.

If you're having more than one of the symptoms listed above, and they persist for more than two weeks, it's time to seek help. Talk to your doctor, pastor or spiritual adviser, or consult a family counselor or professional therapist. It's also important to talk about it with the people you must rely on for support – your family, friends, children, co-workers, etc.

Treatments for depression are surprisingly effective

Up to 80% of those who seek treatment will notice rapid improvement, usually within a few weeks. In addition to medication and "talk therapy", some lifestyle modifications may help get you back on your feet.

Put pleasure on your schedule!

Each day, do something for yourself...from taking a warm bath to going for a walk with a friend...don't cancel this very important appointment! It doesn't need to take an hour...even a few minutes can be effective. The point is, schedule it and do it...every day!

Keep healthy finances!

Worrying about debt and finances is one of the top reasons for clinical depression. Keep your finances in order, or seek help if you're feeling stressed about money. A professional objective can often help you establish a budget and stick to it. Let go of the guilt you may feel about your situation and just resolve to take control, rather than letting it control you!

Limit your caffeine to just a few cups a day. Caffeine may boost your mood temporarily, but some women feel a letdown when it wears off.

Get enough calcium…Research suggests that calcium may help with emotional symptoms of PMS. Good sources of dietary calcium are found on page 41.

Plan ahead. Set aside one day to plan a week's worth of menus. Create your shopping list at the same time. This will eliminate the stress of choosing a healthy dinner option in the midst of the chaos we often feel in the evenings. Take the pressure off yourself to be "perfect". Each meal needn't be a gourmet sensation! This book offers several healthy, balanced, quick and easy options that are sure to please your family. Also, give yourself permission to take a night off. Order pizza, pick up take-out, or pop a frozen, prepared meal in the oven or microwave. When we talk of a healthy, nutritious overall diet…it doesn't mean we can't indulge ourselves every now and again.

Put things into proper perspective. Many women feel pressure to maintain the home and family in the same way their own mothers may have. The world is a different place than it was for our parents' generation. If it's not important to you and your family to have the sheets ironed or the carpets vacuumed daily, then don't make it an issue. Decide what's important to you from a household perspective and then stick to that. It's all about priorities and perspective.

Exercise daily. Activity boosts levels of chemicals in the brain that elevate mood. Even a five-minute walk can help. One of today's fitness trends actually began 5,000 years ago. Yoga means "union of the true self", which points to its special emphasis on the mind/body connection. Yoga combines a series of slow postures with breathing exercises and meditation to achieve numerous physical and mental benefits. Regular yoga practice may help improve circulation and flexibility, and relieve stress for a greater sense of well-being.

Don't forget your girlfriends! A chat with a good friend can have a significant effect on your mood. Sometimes, you may just need a good friend to remind you of your own strengths and to bring you back to a positive place. If you're looking for an emotional "pick-me-up", call a friend who picks you up!

These lifestyle modifications should help curb the occasional depression and help you maintain control over your stress. BUT, clinical depression is a serious disease that requires professional medical attention. If your symptoms don't improve within a few weeks, or you feel out of control…seek professional help right away.

More and more treatments are emerging, including prescription drugs, over-the-counter herbal remedies, talk therapies, exercise programs, counseling endeavors and nutritional programs that can either combat symptoms of mental disorders or help lessen them enough that other treatments may become more effective. According to the *US Center for Mental Health Services*, up to half of all visits to doctors are depression-related, even if depression is never discussed. Problems such as chronic headaches, high blood pressure, fatigue, bowel problems and fibromyalgia can often be related to underlying depression.

Every year, 7 to 10% of Americans suffer from mood disorders, a cluster of mental illnesses best recognized as

Get some sun and fresh air!

Exposure to sunlight triggers the release of melatonin in the brain. Melatonin regulates your sleep and wake cycles, and it can have a powerful effect on energy and mood. And, while you're at it…your body is absorbing Vitamin D, which helps your body better absorb the calcium…are you getting the picture here?

Don't forget your sunscreen!

$\mathscr{G}$et your Bs!

Studies indicate that depressed adults are often lacking sufficient nutrients including Vitamin B$_{12}$ and B$_6$ (see pages 12–14 for dietary sources). It is estimated that, on average, women only get about half as much Vitamin B$_6$ as they should. Both are thought to help regulate moods and protect long-term mental health. If you can't get there with diet, consider a supplement.

depression or mania. Mood disorders have symptoms outside the bounds of normal fluctuations from sadness to happiness. They have potentially-severe consequences. Moreover, disability and suffering are not limited to the patient. Spouses, children, parents, siblings and friends can experience frustration, guilt, anger, financial hardship and many other stressors in their attempts to cope with the affected person's suffering. According to Walter Smitson, PhD, Professor, Department of Psychiatry, University of Cincinnati Medical Center and President & CEO, Central Clinic, Inc., one of the three major areas of mental illness is depression. Dr. Smitson cites the other two areas as bipolar disorder and schizophrenia.

Bipolar disorder, also known as *manic-depressive* illness, is a brain disorder that causes unusual shifts in a person's mood, energy and ability to function. Different from the normal ups and downs that everyone goes through, the symptoms of bipolar disorder are severe. They can result in damaged relationships, poor job or school performance, and even suicide. But there is good news: bipolar disorder can be treated, and people with this illness can lead full and productive lives.

Schizophrenia is the most chronic and disabling of the severe mental disorders. A diagnosis of schizophrenia is often confusing and shocking to families and friends. Many people with schizophrenia experience episodes throughout their lives, losing opportunities for careers and relationships. They are stigmatized by lack of public understanding about the disease. The good news is that newer treatments with fewer side effects have improved the lives of many people with schizophrenia.

A "Recipe" for A Beautiful Mind

While a good wholesome meal with comfort food may not be a cure for the "blues", it may certainly be a cure for the "blahs"! In addition to *eating* comfort food, the entire process of shopping for and preparing it can lift your spirits. Pull out one of your mother's or grandmother's recipes, like the two we have at the end of this chapter, and go for it. Before you start your shopping, dig around in your closets and pull out a few "treasures" that belonged to someone you love and think how you can incorporate them in your cooking or your presentation and serving. Then, of course, while you're out shopping, consider a few new purchases that you can use to add to your kitchen equipment or your table setting. Use this opportunity to put some "Passion" into everyday activities…there's nothing extreme about it!!

Mom's Chicken Cacciatore

Thanks to Dr. Glennis Orloff
Program Director - New Products
Intuition Women's Razor System
Schick-Wilkinson Sword and Energizer Company

Who doesn't love an Italian-inspired hearty meal? Here's a healthier take on a classic favorite. Yes, it's high in calories, but consider that, if eaten with a simple green salad, your entire meal will still be reasonable in calorie count.

INGREDIENTS

4-6	skinned chicken breasts
1 tsp	olive oil
½ tsp	pepper
½ cup	chopped onion
1 clove	garlic, pressed
1 tsp	basil
½ tsp	oregano
3 large	tomatoes – chopped
½ cup	wine vinegar

PREPARATION

- Season breasts with pepper (and a little sea salt if desired) and brown on each side.
- Sauté onion and garlic in olive oil for 4-5 minutes in a skillet.
- Add pepper, tomatoes, oregano and wine and bring to a boil. Cook about 10 minutes until sauce thickens.
- Add in chicken; cook another 10-15 minutes turning chicken until it is done.

  Serve over pasta (approximately ½ pound, before cooking) or rice (approximately 1½ cups before cooking).

NUTRITIONAL ANALYSIS
Serves: 6
Each serving, with pasta, contains approximately:
473 calories
45 g. protein
54 g. carbohydrates
7 g. fat
13% calories from fat
42 mg. calcium

Thanksgiving Turkey

Thanks to Dianne Dunkelman
Founder, Speaking of Women's Health

To give every child born with a cleft the opportunity for a full life.

85+
countries where donor support helps give children new smiles

340+
free cleft repair surgeries performed every day

1,000+
free medical articles and publications we make available

2,100+
Smile Train partner surgeons who donate their time

125,000+
surgeries that friends like you will help provide this year

Plus 1 individual like you who believes in Smile Train!

Light meat
222 calories
42 g. protein
0 g. carbohydrates
5 g. fat
20% calories from fat
30 mg. calcium

t and simple way to cook a
·ipe is terrific for
nd it can cook all afternoon.

RATION

at oven to 450 degrees.

ve giblets and neck.

turkey and pat dry.

ith olive oil.

avity with heel of bread,
stalks, one whole onion,
l, and one apple. You may also
esh sage or rosemary for
flavor.

turkey in heavy foil two
.scrunch it, but not airtight.
in roasting pan 2 inches deep.

at 450^0 according to size, or
neat thermometer reads 180^0
°. Open foil to brown the last
nutes. For easy slicing, cover
oil and let stand after
ing from oven for 15 minutes.

Chapter 6

Build Relationships Your Heart Desires

Your friend is someone who believes you're a good egg — even though she knows you're slightly cracked.

Do not protect yourself by a fence, but rather by your friends.

Czechoslovakian Proverb

Our recipe for healthy relationships
begins very simply...

It Begins with You!

You may have noticed that we started this chapter with two quotes. One reads, "Do not protect yourself by a fence, but rather by your friends." This may actually speak to your physical health; and the other quote, "Your friend is someone who believes you're a good egg — even though she knows you're slightly cracked," can have a huge impact on your emotional well-being! As we discuss in Chapter 2, frequent connections with good friends can boost your immune system and may even avert a second heart attack. Now, that is certainly better protection than a fence! And, a friend who not only has a sense of humor but appreciates your sense of humor and idiosyncracies can certainly boost your emotions and self-esteem! To have good friends, you have to be a good friend; but, be careful not to take that commitment so far that you neglect yourself.

As children, most or all of us were taught the Golden Rule...do unto others as we wish them to do unto us. This worked well for teaching us to share our toys, to say "please" and "thank you" and to treat others with respect.

As we age, our lives and relationships become more complicated. In our never-ending quest to be superwomen, it's not uncommon for us to treat others significantly better than we treat ourselves. We've gotten it backward. Just as we discuss throughout this book, a healthy self-esteem and respect for yourself is the cornerstone of **Building Relationships Your Heart Desires**. Don't think about this as being selfish...think of this as being strong enough physically and mentally to "be there" for friends and family when they need you.

4 "Ingredients" for a Healthy Relationship

Resolve

Think

Success

Action

Resolve

Before you can embrace life with good friends and loving relationships, you must first resolve that this is something worth doing. It takes a commitment to build and maintain a friendship, a marriage or a lasting mother-child bond. If you're feeling lonely or disappointed in a relationship or desire a more meaningful friendship — the first step is to recognize that something is missing, and resolve that you want to make it better. Putting passion behind this resolve will make it easier, and it can also help erase months, or even years, of resentment.

Think

Take a moment to assess your current and/or past relationships. Think about what has "worked" and what has not. If your relationship with your mother isn't all you wish it were, try to think about where it went wrong. Is your mother still angry because you didn't take her advice when you got married? Are you frustrated with all of the "help" your mother gives you about raising your children, managing your marriage and cleaning your house? How about your sister? Are either of you still secretly harboring that feeling that "Dad always liked you best?" Is it possible you're still holding a grudge against your friend who left you out of a gathering? Did your husband hurt your feelings when he gave you "overly" constructive criticism, or worse yet, betrayed your trust? Difficult as it may be, it is important to embrace responsibility for your own actions and reactions. Take time to re-evaluate your own actions, responses, commitment and communication style...what could *you* have done differently? How might that difference have affected the outcome? Remember, you've already resolved that you'd like these relationships to improve. Taking the first step may require more than just a "chat". If the issues are deep-rooted, this may be a good time to consider talking with a professional counselor, therapist or adviser to help sort through your feelings and begin the healing process.

Success

Next, it's time to think about what "success" looks like to you. How will you know when you've built the relationships your heart desires? Once you achieve success, will you know how to maintain it? When dealing with family, try using some techniques of successful relationships you've had in the past. Think about how empowered you felt when you resolved a conflict with a co-worker. Some of our most successful relationships are with people who are not family members. Chances are if you had a disappointment or conflict with a co-worker, a service person or your child's teacher, you resolved it by saying something like, "I feel very disappointed about (whatever issue may have occurred)." You would probably never think of screaming, slamming the door, hanging up the telephone or shutting that person out of your life. So…*why* would you do that with those relationships that are most important to you? Build on the successes you have experienced in other areas when **Building Relationships Your Heart Desires**.

Action

Finally…it's time to create an action plan. Maybe it begins with just one relationship at a time…maybe it begins by making a promise to yourself to send your sister a card to tell her you love her and want her to be part of your life. *(Even though Dad really did love you more! However, Mom loved her more…)* Okay, we're kidding a bit, but a great action plan includes keeping a sense of humor! Whatever your plan of attack…think it through. Remember that action begins with you, and that action requires "change".

In addition to re-building existing relationships, you may consider building a new relationship. Yes, a new relationship does change your life. And, change can be a very good thing. At one of the first Speaking of Women's Health conferences, our now longtime friend and speaker, Ronda Gates, gave a talk about change. She asked the attendees to stand up and look at the person next to them. After about 30 seconds, she then asked everyone to turn around and change something about themselves. When they turned back, their partner was asked to recognize what had been changed. Ronda then pointed out that, as women, the overwhelming majority took

Learn to embrace responsibility and be the person you'd like to be every day...not just on good days.

Put a smile on your face and communicate positive, friendly and supportive messages even when you may not feel your best. Now, look in the mirror...Doesn't that woman smiling back make you feel better?

something "OFF" to make a change, rather than put something "ON". As women, we often perceive change as having something taken away. But, change can also be very positive — something or someone new added to your life. Change will help you grow in your relationships with others, and it can add value to the relationships your heart desires.

What affects our relationships? More opportunities for ACTION

Whether we're 16 or 60, as women, there's one thing we all have in common...hormones! There's no question that your hormonal fluctuations impact your thoughts, feelings, behaviors and moods. BUT...the question is, how are you going to manage it?

"Let's face it...we all have our *days*," as Dr. Robin Smith says. "Whether it's monthly PMS or menopausal symptoms or post-partum changes...it's up to you to decide how to live with these ever-present mood swings and physical symptoms. You can certainly take responsibility for your actions, and not allow yourself to be emotionally hijacked by your hormones. How often have you heard someone make an excuse for rude behavior or disinterest and blame it on PMS...or just a sour mood? Is that how you want to be thought of?"

Think PMS is bad? It could be worse. Sometimes medications may be prescribed that play havoc with our hormones, affecting us emotionally and physically. While undergoing chemotherapy for breast cancer, a long-time Speaking of Women's Health speaker and dear friend, Elaine Boynton, once laughed, "I used to think a bad hair day was awful...until I discovered no-hair days!" Whether your hormonal changes are natural, or the result of medications...put your emotions into perspective and, like Elaine, keep a sense of humor!

In addition, there may be other options. Talk to your doctor about evaluating your hormone levels. We now know that improper balances of estrogen, progesterone and testosterone may negatively impact a woman's emotional, physical, and, even sexual well-being. When we talk about libido, most of us think of sex drives. Libido actually means, "life's energy." If you're lacking desire or energy for life…sexually, physically and even emotionally…your hormones may be the culprit. If you feel that the quality of your life's energy is being compromised…don't wait another minute! Talk to your family doctor or gynecologist about ways to measure and treat hormonal imbalances. Many women are surprised to find that, in addition to estrogen, females also produce testosterone, and, like estrogen, production declines with age. It's the balance of estrogen and testosterone that helps us feel "in balance". If you're just not feeling like your "old self" ask your doctor what options may be available to help put energy back into your life and some passion into your relationships.

"Ingredients" for a Joyful Feast?

How much has been written about our relationship with food? Usually, when we're reading about our relationship with food, it's in the negative context of overindulging. Not in this book!! Our experts believe that food can fuel a passion for life. And, there's no reason these "passion foods" can't be healthy, as well. (Research now shows that a bit of chocolate may be good for our "emotional health, as well as our heart health.")

One way to reconnect with our passionate side is through our senses…all five of them. And, food may be the best way to engage all five senses at once. You smell it, taste it, touch it, see it and hear it…(Think snap, crackle, pop as you sauté those fresh veggies!) That passion can begin when you walk through your neighborhood market or grocery store and marvel at the beauty of nature's bounty on display in the produce department. Talk about beautiful colors and wonderful smells! A nice way to build a "healthy habits" relationship with your children, is by taking them through the grocery store and sharing your enthusiasm for these colors and aromas. Maybe, as adults, their emotional connections will take them back to this positive experience with you. And, besides, it sure beats going through the grocery store telling your kids "Don't touch!" Putting joy or passion into everyday activities certainly increases life's energy.

A Rose by Any Other Name...

While the sense of smell is important to men, research has proven that smell is the strongest sense for women. Just think how many of your emotional connections are brought to mind when you smell something that reminds you of a treasured moment in your childhood or a cherished memory of a grandparent's home.

Can foods really fuel passion?

Chocolate

What is it about chocolate that makes so many of us swoon? Sometimes we get these intense cravings for chocolate. We may be feeling moody and irritable, even depressed, but once we eat some chocolate, we feel better. Why? It turns out that chocolate is a mood-enhancer. Chocolate contains phenethylamine (PEA), which stimulates the nervous system, triggering the release of endorphins, opiate-like compounds that dull pain and give a sense of well-being. But the jury is still out on whether the high fat and sugar content are additional factors for this response. There are also chemicals in chocolate that increase the activity of dopamine, a neurotransmitter directly associated with feelings of romance. (Think about why so many boxes of chocolate are given for Valentine's Day!) Additionally, chocolate can also boost brain levels of serotonin, the happy neurotransmitter, especially in women who tend to be more sensitive to chocolate than men. Another way chocolate can make us feel good is by inhibiting the natural breakdown of anandamide, a neurotransmitter normally found in small amounts in the brain, which can produce a feeling of euphoria. While scientists continue to study whether the concentrations of these chemicals present in chocolate can actually produce a significant effect on our moods, many women will contend that research aside, satisfying a chocolate craving can work wonders.

Cinnamon

Although the way to a man's heart may be through his stomach, the way into his arms may be found before the meal, via his nose. Neurologist Alan R. Hirsch, MD, from the Smell & Taste Treatment and Research Foundation in Chicago, has studied the results of certain scents which change blood flow to the genital areas of men and women. The most dramatic results were achieved in men with a combination of lavender and pumpkin pie, which increased blood flow by as much as 40%. A combination of black licorice and donut scents showed a 32% increase in the blood flow. None of the scents tested had as significant an impact on women. The smell of pumpkin pie includes the spices ginger, cinnamon and clove — all warming, spicy scents. Ginger (Zingiber officinalis) and cinnamon (Cinnamomum zeylanicum) essential oils are both considered to be aphrodisiacs with energizing properties.

Scent-sational

Scent is a simple way to set the mood for romance, whether applied as a perfume or diffused through a room. Our sense of smell is primal. The nerve endings in the nose are barely separated from the limbic system of the brain, the "old brain" that serves as the center for our basic instincts — including sexual desire. What better place to start a romance than at a juncture between the present moment and the beginning of time?

Whatever your pleasure, it's really all about indulging yourself with something that makes you feel special, or something that you crave or truly, passionately enjoy. But, of course, keep in mind that great things come in small packages! Whatever your preferred indulgence …whether it's chocolate or aged cheeses…enjoy them in moderation! The best relationships are lasting relationships…and, as we said at the beginning of this chapter, it begins with you. Do unto others, but first, do unto yourself. Keep yourself healthy and vital and you'll bring much more to that loving relationship your heart desires!

When you're rekindling a relationship with your mom, sisters or friends…or if you're making new friends…invite them over for an afternoon tea or dessert party. Here are some recipes no relationship can resist.

Apple Crisp

Thanks to Debbie Hodges
VP, Divisional Merchandise Manager, Wal-Mart

The name is misleading, any fruit or combination works with this recipe. Try plums and pears, cranberry and apple, add figs, dates, currants…got the picture?

INGREDIENTS

8	tart apples, or any fruit
¼ cup	water
1 Tbsp	vanilla extract
1 tsp	cinnamon or nutmeg
½ cup	sugar
6 Tbsp	butter or margarine, cut into pats
¼ cup	flour
¼ cup	instant oats, uncooked

PREPARATION

- Preheat oven to 325 degrees.

- Peel fruit and cut into bite-sized chunks. Place in deep baking dish, coated with cooking spray. Sprinkle with cinnamon or nutmeg. Combine water and vanilla, and pour over fruit mixture.

- In food processor, combine sugar, flour, oats and butter. Process until well blended and crumbly. Sprinkle topping onto fruit mixture, pressing down lightly. Bake at 325°, uncovered, for 35 minutes, or until topping is golden. Remove from oven and let cool 10 minutes before serving.

- If made ahead of time, toss apples or fruit with lemon juice prior to placing in dish.

NUTRITIONAL ANALYSIS, apples only
Servings: 8
Each serving contains approximately:
241 calories
1 g. protein
39 g. carbohydrates
10 g. fat
37% calories from fat, but…only 22% from saturated fat
29 mg. calcium
4.4 g. dietary fiber

*Nutritional analysis will vary for other fruits. This is for apple crisp.

The Dearest of
FRIENDS
A SPECIAL POEM
BY EMILY MATTH...

Chocolate Mint Cake

Thanks to Lynn Picard
Executive Vice President/General Manager
Lifetime Television Network

This is a featured favorite from Canyon Ranch Health Resorts, who provide recipes for our quarterly newsletter. It's sure to please your loved ones, and is a terrific dessert for any occasion that calls for CHOCOLATE!

INGREDIENTS

1 cup	unbleached all purpose flour
1/2 cup	unsweetened cocoa powder
3/4 cup	sugar
1 tsp	baking powder
	pinch salt
2 Tbsp	unsweetened applesauce
1/2 cup	low-fat milk (1%)
1 tsp	vanilla extract
1 tsp	mint extract
1 Tbsp	instant coffee mixed with 2 Tbsp water
2 jars	baby food pureed prunes
1/2 oz.	semi-sweet chocolate morsels, melted
2	egg whites
2 Tbsp	non-fat chocolate fudge sauce
	powdered sugar for garnish

NUTRITIONAL ANALYSIS
Servings: 12
Each serving contains approximately:
148 calories
3 g. protein
30 g. carbohydrates
1 g. fat
6% calories from fat
51 mg. calcium

PREPARATION

- Preheat the oven to 300 degrees.
- Spray a 10-inch cake pan with non-stick cooking spray and lightly dust with flour.
- Sift together all of the dry ingredients into a large mixing bowl.
- In a small bowl, mix the applesauce, milk, vanilla and mint extracts, coffee, prunes and chocolate. Add to the dry ingredients and mix well.
- Beat the egg whites in a small, non-plastic bowl until stiff. Fold into the cake batter.
- Spread the batter in the prepared pan. Bake in the preheated oven for 35 to 40 minutes, or until a knife inserted in the middle of the cake comes out clean.
- Remove the cake from the oven and cool on a rack. When the cake is cool, spread the top with the non-fat chocolate sauce. Sprinkle the top with powdered sugar just before serving. The easiest way to cut this cake into 12 equal servings is to first cut it into quarters. Cut each quarter into 3 equal wedges.

Chapter 7

Trust Your Gut

"It is through science that we prove,
but through intuition that we discover."

Henri Poincare

Our recipe for healthy digestion begins very simply…

Trust Your Gut!

*I*ntuition can be a powerful message. It's that voice inside us that often leads us in a new direction. Many experts believe that this "inner voice" possesses the potential to enrich our lives. That may be the case, but it's up to us to listen and interpret what the voice is telling us.

In the case of our "gut", when that voice is speaking…there's no mistaking that it's telling us when we've got a problem. Some experts describe the woman's stomach as her "second brain," because it often sends signals that require our attention.

Indeed, the "gut" can be a barometer of overall emotional and physical health. Women frequently talk about the importance of listening to *"female intuition"* or *"trusting your gut"*, and the saying has both literal and figurative meanings. Research now shows that there are more neurotransmitters in the 20 feet of your "gut" than there are in your brain. So, when you have *"butterflies in your stomach"*, or you just have that *"feeling in your gut"*, it really is a legitimate mind/body connection. Psychologically, intuition can be a great thing. Physiologically, it can create problems in your gut like gas, heartburn, indigestion and IBS *(irritable bowel syndrome)*.

Some simple lifestyle changes may help prevent the symptoms of heartburn.

Don't eat just before bedtime.

Chew gum to stimulate the flow of saliva, washing juices back into the stomach and helping to neutralize the acid.

Eat several smaller meals throughout the day to avoid overfilling the stomach.

Maintain a healthy weight and regular physical activity.

Avoid smoking and excessive alcohol and caffeine intake.

Avoid tight-fitting clothing.

Over & Out

In it's simplest terms, our digestive system is a series of tubes and valves that leads to the stomach and then eventually through the organs that eliminate what our bodies cannot use. As we eat the food, chewing it and swallowing it, it travels to the stomach, where acids and chemicals break it down so that it can pass into the intestines, where key nutrients are absorbed into the bloodstream. Food that's chewed in the mouth enters into the esophagus, a muscular tube about nine inches long. At the top of the esophagus is a small valve that relaxes to let food enter the esophagus and also to keep it from going where it's not supposed to go, or "down the wrong pipe". At the bottom of the esophagus is a stronger valve that relaxes to let food into the stomach. When the lower valve fails to work properly, food backs up into the esophagus causing a variety of symptoms.

The effective operation of our digestive system depends on many factors – everything from the amount of acid in our stomach, to our stress levels, to what we eat and when…even what we're wearing when we eat. This may be a simplified version of a very technical biological process, but intestinal distress runs the gamut from a mild discomfort caused by occasional overeating to chronic heartburn or even life-altering ulcers or irritable bowel syndrome. The bottom line is…it's not a subject to be taken lightly. Unfortunately, many people ignore digestive issues. Fewer than 25% of those who suffer weekly from intestinal symptoms seek medical treatment. For those who do seek help, it's available in a variety of forms…from education to lifestyle changes and new and powerful medications to bring relief.

Heartburn – Don't let the pot boil over

Nearly everyone suffers from occasional heartburn. If it happens more than once a week, it may cause a more serious medical problem. Gastroesophageal reflux disease (GERD) occurs when a rind of muscle at the base of the esophagus weakens or opens at the wrong time, allowing stomach acids into the esophagus, causing the burning feeling we know as heartburn.

If lifestyle changes aren't enough to keep heartburn at bay, several types of medicines are available. They work on the same principles: reducing the amount of acid that the stomach and esophagus are exposed to in order to reduce the likelihood of setting off the burning sensations and other symptoms.

The most common medicines

Over-the-counter antacids such as Tums®, Maalox®, Rolaids®, Pepto Bismol® and Mylanta®, neutralize the acid in the stomach and are good for relieving symptoms quickly. The liquid forms may work fast, but tablets may often be more convenient. The effect of these antacids may not last long, so repeating doses may be required for relief.

Over-the-counter and prescription H_2 blockers, such as Pepcid AC® and Zantac® work by blocking histamine receptors (that's what H_2 stands for). These receptors stimulate the production of the stomach acids, and by blocking them, the stomach makes less acid, reducing the likelihood of heartburn.

Proton Pump Inhibitors (PPI), such as the newer over-the-counter (Prilosec OTC®) and prescription drugs (Prilosec®, Prevacid® and Nexium®), are powerful substances that block or suppress acid production in the

Heartburn or Heart attack?

Symptoms can be similar, and if there is the slightest question, please seek medical attention immediately.

Some foods naturally contain more acid than others or, once eaten, trigger its production in the stomach.

Do you know which ones are troublesome for you?

Keeping a food diary will help you pay attention to foods that are most likely, in your life, to set off your heartburn symptoms. Try to avoid them in the future.

cells that "pump" acid into the stomach. Some studies also find that they can decrease heartburn-related symptoms, including shortness of breath, hoarseness, chronic cough and laryngitis. *Remember, these are medications in pill form, and not an actual pump.* Once the drugs are at work, they can relieve or prevent symptoms for up to 24 hours.

Other Prescription Drugs: Doctors also have access to so-called prokinetic medicines that help heal the painful swelling in the esophagus, and they're typically prescribed for long-term use. Other drugs can speed up digestion, keeping food in the stomach for shorter periods of time, so that reflux has less of a chance to occur, while still others can protect the mucous lining of the esophagus to keep it healthy and functioning.

As with all drug treatments, talk with your doctor or pharmacist about risks, benefits and possible side effects.

In severe cases of GERD or hiatal hernia, doctors might have to perform surgery to repair the valves that control the flow of contents and acid between the stomach and esophagus.

Trigger Foods
Common foods linked to heartburn may include:

✔ Coffee

✔ Fatty or spicy foods

✔ Carbonated beverages

✔ Peppermint or spearmint

✔ Citrus fruits

✔ Tomatoes

✔ Whole milk

✔ Onions

Chocolate – a word about chocolate…unfortunately, for some people, chocolate may be a trigger. But, since most women consider chocolate "an essential food group", Robin Miller, MD, suggests eating a small piece of chocolate, instead of a small box!

While some foods may trigger heartburn or physical reaction, do not mistake this for something much more serious, and potentially deadly, a **food allergy.** See page 96.

Everybody's Got It!
Okay, who hasn't experienced gas? As "mature" as we get, the thought often elicits giggles or brings to mind embarrassment. For millions of adults, it's no laughing matter. The fact is, on average, our bodies produce one to three pints of gas daily, and we pass it, on average, 14 times a day. Gas is produced in three ways:

1. by the air we swallow when we eat, drink and even talk;
2. by stubborn foods such as carbohydrates which may be difficult for our bodies to digest; and
3. through bacteria that move from our colon to our small intestine.

What can you do to reduce gas and relieve the painful symptoms?
✔ Identify the foods that cause you difficulty. Some offenders may include beans, cabbage, Brussels sprouts, broccoli and asparagus. These contain a sugar called raffinose, a major trigger of gas. It's important to realize that these foods may cause a problem occasionally. If one of these foods is a constant source of pain for you, talk to your doctor or pharmacist about precautions you can take when you eat this food.

✔ Many starchy foods (including potatoes, wheat and corn) produce gas during digestion. Rice, however, does not, which is why pediatricians tell Moms to feed it to their children who have upset stomachs or diarrhea.

✔ Drink from a glass. Carbonated beverages contain gas. Some carbonated gas may escape when poured into a glass rather than being consumed from a can or bottle.

Constipation is a common problem that can cause discomfort, bloating and pain. Constipation generally refers to stools that are infrequent, dry or hard, or difficult to pass. Unlike conventional thinking, there is no "right" number of daily or weekly bowel movements. It's important to understand what your "normal" schedule is, and what is regular for you. This regularity may vary slightly depending on what you eat, how active you are and other factors, but in general, you should maintain a fairly regular schedule.

It is estimated that fewer than 5% of Americans consume the recommended amounts of fiber in their diets. The average woman eats only about 12 grams per day, well below the recommended 25 to 35 grams. Fiber is one of the most important ingredients of a healthy diet. One of the best ways to get fiber is by eating more fruit. Of the hundreds of plant foods that provide fiber, the luscious apricot is but one tasty example. Like most fruits, the fiber content is intensified when dried. Three fresh apricots provide almost 2 grams of fiber, but 3½ ounces of dried apricots provide nearly 8 grams. Fiber is essential for digestive tract health.

Many factors may affect your regularity:

Women may be affected by hormonal changes brought on by pregnancy, the menstrual cycle and menopause.

Some medicines may trigger constipation, including antidepressants, pain medications, antihistamines and calcium or iron supplements. Talk to your doctor or pharmacist if you take these medications regularly, to determine if you need to take action to help avoid the discomfort of constipation.

To maintain regularity, doctors recommend eating a diet rich in fiber (25 to 35 grams daily), drinking plenty of water and maintaining physical activity. It's not difficult to get the recommended fiber amounts in your daily diet. A breakfast cereal fortified with fiber, 6 daily servings of fruits and vegetables, and a healthy snack of dried fruit or a handful of almonds will hit the mark.

Fiber is an essential part of a healthy diet. Fiber adds bulk to the diet and helps stool move easily out of the body. This is especially helpful for people with constipation. In addition, fiber adds substance to the stool, which can help clear up diarrhea. Friendly bacteria in the intestines love fiber and use it as a food source. A diet high in fiber will also help the good bacteria to grow and protect us from the harmful bacteria.

Some excellent food sources of fiber include...
cinnamon, raspberries, mustard greens, collard greens, broccoli, celery, red chili peppers, fennel bulb, grapefruit, cauliflower, cabbage, green beans, eggplant, strawberries, split peas and lentils.

It is important to increase your fiber intake gradually, over the course of several weeks. Any sudden change in diet may bring on temporary discomfort. Also, increase your water intake to help aid in the processing of the fiber while your body adjusts.

If you need to add a supplement, several over-the-counter remedies are available. Talk to your pharmacist.

When to see the doctor

If you've had a sudden change in your bowel habits, or if you notice blood in your stool, see your doctor. It may be nothing serious, but these and other changes could be a sign of cancer or other severe illness. Any change accompanied by weight loss, severe pain or bloating requires a call to the doctor.

Colon cancer

Facts: Colon cancer, also called colorectal cancer, is the third most common cancer in women (and men). Like several other cancers, it's often a "silent" disease because it may exist without symptoms. However, it is a very preventable cancer because early detection and removal of polyps in the colon and rectum may prevent the development of cancer.

Symptoms:

- Rectal bleeding, blood in the stool
- Change in bowel habits
- Cramping pain in the lower abdomen

Early Detection: The tests used to screen for colorectal cancer have strange-sounding names, such as sigmoidoscopy, colonoscopy, barium enema and fecal occult blood tests. Basically, they're all tests that either examine the insides of the colon and rectum to look for polyps (tissue growths) or test for signs of blood in the stool. Once a woman turns 50 (and sometimes earlier), she needs a screening exam for colon cancer. *The most thorough screening is a colonoscopy (the gold standard), which, many gastroenterologists and colorectal surgeons feel should be repeated every 5 years, if normal. It may be repeated sooner if an abnormality is found.* Another common screening test is the fecal occult blood test that can be done yearly, but should be coupled with a sigmoidoscopy every 3 to 5 years. A double contrast barium enema may be substituted every 5 years. A digital rectal exam, usually performed during regular checkups or annual gynecological exams, involves a physician inserting a finger into the rectum to feel for normal tissue. *Those with a family history of colon cancer need to be tested earlier and more often.* Some doctors believe that African Americans may be at higher risk for colon cancer, and therefore may be screened earlier and more often. *Speak to your doctor about your risk factors.*

Food Allergies

We've all heard the headlines of a death that occurs when someone who is unknowingly allergic eats a nut or its by-product. Fortunately, most food allergies aren't this serious. The main symptoms are wheezing, hives, nausea, diarrhea or discomfort. Some people may be allergic to foods and not even know it. Any time you eat something that results in hives, rash, itchy throat, swollen lips or tongue or difficulty breathing…go to the hospital immediately. It is imperative that a health care provider determine whether you are having a "reaction" or an "allergy". Whether your reactions are mild or severe, the only long-term solution is to avoid the food that makes you react. This isn't always easy because people with food allergies are rarely allergic to just one food. It's more commonly a whole group, such as nuts, shellfish or certain grains. And, some need not consume the actual food to have a reaction. It's possible that a bowl or utensil that was used for the offending ingredient, if not properly washed, may trigger a response.

For severe allergic reactions, call 911 immediately if you aren't able to get the symptoms under control as directed by your physician. Many carry injections of epinephrine to reverse symptoms rapidly.

For milder cases, if you suspect a food reaction, keep a log of what you eat and what symptoms occur. Be specific. Don't just write "salad" if you actually ate spinach with hard-boiled eggs, almonds, raisins and an oil and vinegar dressing. Note the physical symptoms that occur.

Many find that common intestinal discomfort is a result of lactose intolerance (the body's inability to tolerate lactose found in milk and dairy products). This can be a challenge for women, who need their calcium for strong bones. Products are available for these conditions. Talk to your doctor or pharmacist.

Yogurt

*H*ave you ever wondered how plain milk becomes rich, creamy yogurt? Well, the secret is a bacterial culture that gets added to the milk. The bacteria eat the milk sugar and give yogurt its tart flavor and thick texture. Even more interesting is that the bacteria used to make yogurt are the same kind as the friendly bacteria found in our digestive tracts.

By eating yogurt, we are helping to replenish the supplies of beneficial bacteria in our own bodies. These bacteria not only protect us from infections from "harmful" bacteria, they may also provide relief from digestive discomfort. Sufferers given foods with these bacteria report less painful bloating and gas than before. Low-fat yogurt is a tasty and convenient healthy snack.

Pork Loin with Cherry Stuffing

Thanks to April Armstrong, Assistant Marketing Manager
Customer Marketing, Wal-Mart Team
Kellogg's

This festive dish is perfect for entertaining, or for a holiday treat. Substitute any dried fruit for cherries, for a different taste. The end result is a beautiful spiral that makes an appealing presentation.

INGREDIENTS

$\frac{1}{3}$ cup	wild rice
1 cup	water
2 tsp	snipped fresh rosemary
$\frac{1}{2}$ tsp	salt
$1\frac{1}{2}$ cup	coarsely chopped dried tart cherries, divided into two portions of $\frac{3}{4}$ cup each (cranberries, blueberries, apricot & prunes all work)
4 lb.	pork loin roast
1 cup	chopped onion
1 tsp	olive oil
2 Tbsp	snipped fresh parsley
2 tsp	snipped fresh thyme
	pepper, to taste
$\frac{1}{4}$ cup	red or white cooking wine

Optional: 1/4 cup walnuts
(almonds or pecans also work)

NUTRITIONAL ANALYSIS
10 servings, each approximately 5 oz. meat
364 calories
41 g. protein
20 g. carbohydrates
12 g. fat
30% calories from fat
47 mg. calcium

PREPARATION

- Preheat oven to 325 degrees.
- In a small pan, combine water, rice, rosemary and salt. Bring to a boil and reduce heat. Cover and simmer for 40 to 45 minutes or until rice is tender. Remove from heat. Set aside.
- Spread the butterflied roast open and cover with plastic wrap. Pound with a meat mallet to $\frac{1}{2}$" to $\frac{3}{4}$" thickness. Remove the plastic wrap and set the meat aside.
- In a large skillet, cook onion in olive oil until tender. Stir in parsley, thyme, and pepper, nuts and cherries (or other dried fruit). Add wine and cook, stirring until most of liquid is evaporated.
- Spread sauce over surface of the roast and roll up from the long side. Tie with string. Insert meat thermometer. Roast meat in oven in shallow pan for two hours, until thermometer registers 155°. Remove from oven and let stand, covered for 15 minutes. Temperature should rise an additional 5°.
- Remove the string and slice into 10 portions. Serve with warm fruit sauce poured over top.

Brown Rice Medley

Thanks to Mary Wilson
Universal Sisters Spokesperson

This is basically stir fried brown rice with veggies, which can be a one dish meal or a full family dish, ala oriental, but is very healthy.

INGREDIENTS

4 cups brown rice, cooked
(for every cup of rice, use two cups of water)

1 clove garlic
(chopped and add to rice while boiling)

½ cup onion (1 medium)
(same as garlic)

4 cups veggies...we used yellow squash, broccoli, red & green peppers and carrots...***We love the color!***

salt
(add pinch to boiling water and rice)

PREPARATION

• Rinse and then let rice boil, once it boils, put lid on and lower flame, so rice will simmer.

• Stir fry veggies, add onion and garlic to flavor. Do not overcook. In fact, do not cook veggies until rice is ready.

• You may add cilantro and any other herbs you want at the last minute when you put the rice in. Cilantro adds a great taste.

Note: Brown rice has a great nutty flavor. To serve, put the rice on a platter, and add the veggies on top....the color is very pretty, and thus the name "Brown Rice Medley"

NUTRITIONAL ANALYSIS, using ingredients listed above
4 servings, each approximately 1-cup serving contains:
325 calories
7 g. protein
56 g. carbohydrates
9 g. fat
25% calories from fat
63 mg. calcium

Chapter 8

Sandwich Generation

"First keep the peace within yourself, then you can also bring peace to others."

Thomas a Kempis

Our recipe for finding balance
in life begins very simply...

Have a heart of gold and a spine of steel!

A cup of consideration for others, a cup of commitment to community, a cup of respect for the family, a cup of responsibility in the workplace... and the most important ingredient...an entire quart of self nurturing. Self nurturing includes healthy eating, physical activity, proper health screenings, spirituality, meaningful relationships, beauty care and pampering.

It's no secret that, today, women are busier than ever. In fact, the idea that women are "multi-taskers" takes on a whole new meaning. Let's look at the life of today's woman. She may be a "finance manager", budgeting for her home and family; balancing a career; raising kids; caring for aging parents. Running one household can be challenging enough, but today's busy, on-the-go woman often faces the challenge of multiple households. She may be spending much of her day thinking about the health care and nutrition of aging parents and communicating with college-aged kids about establishing their first home away from home, and maintaining their nutrition and general health. Let's face it...Women are BUSY!

At Speaking of Women's Health, we've asked women across the country, "What does pampering mean to you?" Overwhelmingly, the answer we get is the same..."Time!" "We need more time!"

According to Kate Hamilton, sleep expert at Canyon Ranch Health Resort, "When women get overwhelmed and overly busy, many cut back on sleep, exercise and healthy eating. This is an option that will leave you feeling more overwhelmed and less successful. Sleepless nights and restless days aren't a good idea long term, either."

What NOT to skimp on...

Sleep

Time with
your spouse

Alone time for
yourself

Family time

Health Screenings

Why are we all so busy?

Today, women enjoy so many opportunities and great potential for satisfaction — personally, at home and at work. Some of those great options that often tempt us may include a fun new project at work, volunteering to lead a child's field trip, making appetizers for your husband's office party or chairing a committee at your place of worship or neighborhood association. With all of these opportunities, there is also the chance to "overdo it". That's why it's more important than ever to make personal relaxation time a priority. For Sandwich Generation women, in particular, making these choices can influence their ability to live life with passion.

According to a recent study, 88% of women, both working and non-working, feel they are responsible for taking care of the people in their families. And, if you are part of the Sandwich Generation, one of the 22 million US households who are involved in caring for an aging loved one, then you know all too well the stress and frustration which can arise from trying to do too much. Again, it's all about *"keeping the peace within yourself"*.

What is the Sandwich Generation?

The Sandwich Generation is comprised of working adults, often in their 30s, 40s, and 50s, who are caught between the demands of caring for aging adults and raising their children. The ranks of the Sandwich Generation are growing. Look at these numbers…you're not alone! More than two-thirds of women with children under the age of 18 years are in the workforce. As much as one-third of the US workforce has caregiving responsibilities for older relatives.

Members of the Sandwich Generation share many concerns...

✔ the need for information and referrals to child care providers and elder care services

✔ strained relationships with elderly parents caused by caretaking responsibilities

✔ concerns about leaving young children with caregivers

✔ a need to learn better parenting and communication skills

✔ stressed relationships with spouses

✔ health problems caused by stress and burnout

✔ a need for alternative work options that allow them to work outside the traditional 9 to 5, Monday – Friday week

✔ the need to incorporate exercise and relaxation into their lives

According to the Family Caregiver Alliance
www.caregiver.org

| Kids |
| Home |
| Career |
| Pet |
| Spouse |
| Self |

OOPS!
In a national survey, this pyramid shows how women ranked their priorities.

Given the tiny bit allotted to "self", this can be a "recipe" for anger, depression and resentment.

Instead, try the "recipe" on this page for serenity, self-esteem and vitality.

"Ingredients" for serenity

✔ **Relaxation.** Use yoga, visual imagery and quiet time to gradually relax every muscle, head to toe.

✔ **Deep breathing.** It's easy to learn and you can use it wherever and whenever you need it.

✔ **Healthy diet.** Your body requires properly-balanced nutrition. Vitamins A, C & E are important. So are your ZZZZZ's…a good night's sleep is a "meal" in itself.

✔ **A journal or "stress diary".** Keeping a journal can release stress, and help you organize and fulfill your creativity.

Empower yourself and family members
Empower yourself to take advantage of outside resources, acknowledging that the relationship between you and your parents may actually now be "role reversal". Also, encourage other family members to embrace the satisfaction of honoring their elders. In addition to sharing the responsibilities of elder care, think about the wonderful message you are sending to your children. Hopefully, you are helping them build a sensitivity and skill set that they will use in the future…*your future!* Here are some ingredients for self-esteem.

✔ **Don't try to do it all yourself.** Most communities have ample resources for assisting Sandwich Generation families. From respite care to meal programs, get in touch with area non-profit and government agencies to see what services are available to your family.

✔ **Remember that this is difficult for your parents, as well.** It's important to put yourself in the position of the person for whom you are caring, and to do all you can to help your aging loved one maintain his or her sense of dignity and any independence that is possible.

✔ **Try to work with other family members.** It's important to involve siblings and other relatives, who may not be primary caregivers. If they live too far away to help with daily care, enlist their support in major decisions. If they are local, but in other households, they can be important in providing relief in caretaking activities. Wherever they live, keeping them involved can help avoid resentment and misunderstanding among family members.

✔ **Keep lines of communication open.** If you foresee a time when you will need to take time off from work, try to be as forthright with your employer as possible.

✔ **Communicate with your family and friends about your needs.** Don't let bad feelings simmer. Try to work them out before they become more serious.

Celebrate yourself

Although much of your time may require activities that revolve around others, it is essential that you maintain the things that you feel passionate about in your life. These things that bring you joy are the "ingredients" for your vitality.

✔ If you're passionate about canoeing, bike trips, weekends in the mountains or your family vacation to the beach, make plans in advance to "cover" your elder care responsibilities so that you do not have to sacrifice this pleasure. Think of it in the same way that you would have made thoughtful decisions about babysitters when your children were young.

✔ If you're passionate about "date night" with your spouse, don't give up that dinner and a movie or concert. You will feel fresh and young again and full of vitality after an evening out. If arranging an evening away is too complicated, consider a lunch date and a matinee.

Take care of yourself

Use your time wisely, being sure it includes "pampering moments" for yourself. Many caretakers feel guilty about taking time out for themselves. However, it is critical that the caretaker make her own emotional health and well-being a priority in order to have the peace from within.

The best way to restore balance and regain quality of life is to decide where you're going to put your energy – both physical and emotional.

✔ Hopefully you're passionate about looking good and feeling your best. There are also lots of fun "everyday" beauty makeovers you can do at home. Yes, you can give yourself a manicure, pedicure and, thanks to advances in home hair coloring, you can give yourself a fresh look. (See tips for healthy hair, skin and nails in Chapter 9.) Don't rule out treating yourself to a bit of luxury, like a massage, at the spa.

✔ If you're passionate about your friendships, don't let them drift away because you're "so busy". Even 30 minutes walking and laughing with a friend can refresh your vitality. Most friends are thrilled to help ...you just need to communicate and ask for that help. You might even consider telling them to surprise you with a funny card or a cartoon they have clipped from a newspaper or magazine. Women often hesitate to say what they need or to give specific direction. It's important to be explicit. Saying, "I'm tired", and expecting a spouse or sibling to suggest that you take a spa day, is a weak strategy. Saying, "I'm tired, and it would really help me if you could take care of Mom so I could have a day off," will likely yield better results. One of our staff members uses this personal story as an example that "it's not possible to over-communicate". One day when she was riding on a bus from one airport terminal to the next, she noticed a sign painted on the tarmac. It read, "Buses: Yield to Aircraft." She laughed to herself, thinking... *"Is it really necessary to communicate something that should seem so obvious to the driver? Do we really need to tell a bus to yield to a 747 aircraft?"* The following week, there was a brief article in the newspaper describing how a luggage van had collided with a plane. *Hmmmmm.*

A "Recipe" for Balance
Assembling the "Ingredients"...

Is simplicity the answer?

If your life feels too busy or too complex, maybe you're putting too much pressure on yourself. Using the "ingredients" or tips in this chapter might help you make some decisions. Need a little help getting started? A good place to begin is to take a look at how you spend your time. Keep a journal for two weeks, including weekends. At the end of the two weeks, divide your time into categories. These categories may include work, caring for children, commuting, cooking, cleaning, caring for others. How many of these things are "musts" and how many can you delegate or do less often?

What can come off the list?

At least, what can come off *your* list? While many tasks may not be able to go away completely, think about what you can delegate: driving to the cleaners (have pick-up service), cooking one night a week (delegate or go out), grocery shopping (delegate), house repair (hire out), car washing (go to the car wash). Think of 10 tasks to delegate off your list and write them down. Here's a great place to put some creativity into your thinking. One woman told us that she struggled to keep up with the laundry for her family of four, which included two teenage girls. As a solution, Jane offered an "exchange" deal to her friend, Mary, who had a very different schedule. Mary agreed to wash and fold Jane's family laundry each week, if Jane would cook three meals a week for Mary and pick up extra groceries while shopping for her own family.

The best way to restore balance and regain quality of life is to decide where you're going to put your energy – both physical and emotional. Make choices that are life-extending. Make it a point to designate time for yourself. Allow yourself to enjoy your exercise routine, some time alone and, of course, a bit of self-pampering. Have the courage to follow the airline's safety instructions, "If you're traveling with small children and we experience decompression in the cabin, please put your oxygen mask on first!"

Get Your ZZZZZZZZs

Though we still don't fully understand how sleep affects our physiology, we know we need it for our health and survival. It refreshes our bodies and restores our minds. The right amount of sleep keeps us alert and energetic. A lack of it makes us irritable and forgetful. So it is essential that we get as much sleep as we need to make us feel good. We love this "recipe" for better sleep: avoid exercise, caffeine and heavy meals just before bedtime. Establish a soothing nighttime routine like reading or relaxing in a warm bath. Sweet dreams!

Recipe for Saving Time
Meals on the Go...

It is possible to avoid the late afternoon or after-work urge to binge on unhealthy foods. This is especially true if you are armed with the knowledge that there are plenty of easy-to-make meals that come together in just a few minutes and complete nutrition drinks for busy, on-the-go women. Not having time to sit down for a meal shouldn't mean you skip a meal. Your local markets and grocery stores offer plenty of nutritious and convenient solutions.

Easy-to-make meals
Experts agree that there are many benefits to cooking at home, including stress-free family time together, substantial food-dollar savings and improved meal nutrition. This can be as simple as satisfying every appetite by establishing a "personal choice night". Allow a family member to choose his or her favorite nutritious frozen meal. Here are other time-saving tips.

Plan in advance
Have a weekly meal plan and shop for the groceries you'll need. Choose simple supper recipes on busy days. In 20 minutes, you can grill or bake a piece of fresh salmon; make rice and combine with chopped red pepper, yellow pepper and asparagus sauteed in olive oil and seasoned salt; make a salad of baby romaine and dried cranberries, bleu cheese, avocado, calamata olives and a vinegrette dressing. Your guests will never guess that this "gourmet" meal was such a breeze!

Delegate
Decide how many nights each week you're going to cook. For some, 3 is more than enough, for others, 6 is just fine. Then, divide responsibility for the other nights among family members. Make it their decision, their responsibility. Decision-making is empowering and it takes the work "off your plate". Some families have rules that the cook is exempt from cleaning up. Or the shopper gets to shower while the groceries are unloaded and put away.

Make extra

When you do have extra time to cook, make enough for more than one meal. Prepare items on the weekend that you can reinvent into a fun meal on weekdays. If you're roasting a chicken on the weekend, buy several and then use the extra meat for a quick pasta or pot pie during the week. Making lasagna? Make two and freeze one. It's great to have on hand for your own family, or to offer a friend who is stressed. Some neighbors actually have a dinner swap. One night each week, all those involved cook one extra family-sized serving. The next morning, it's swap time! Leftovers are great if they're not yours! Frozen dinners also make it that much easier if someone else is coming in to care for your children or an elderly loved one.

Use your Crock-Pot or slow cooker

Get up five minutes early and toss in a beef roast, onions, potatoes and carrots. Sprinkle some herbs and pop on the lid. Cook on low for 8 to 10 hours. You'll love the aroma you'll experience when you arrive home that evening to a meal ready to eat!

Keep the cupboard stocked

Make sure that you keep your pantry stocked with staples that you like to blend with your fresh ingredients. It's easier to find inspiration when you've got choices. Make it fun.

Challenge yourself to use a staple you haven't used in awhile. *Savor the following recipes and see if there are some fun ingredients you don't often use, or maybe have never used before.*

Chick Pea & Corn Patties

Sharron Kornegay
Public Affairs Manager
Ross Products Division, Abbott Laboratories

This is a terrific healthy alternative to a classic burger, or just a great vegetarian meal. Serve with Salsa (see page 131) or on a bun with aioli sauce or your favorite condiments. The flavor will surprise you!

INGREDIENTS

2 tsp	olive oil
1½ cup	fresh or frozen corn kernels
1 cup	chopped onion
1 tsp	thyme
1 can	chick peas (garbanzo beans), rinsed and drained
¼ cup	fresh breadcrumbs
¼ cup	instant oats (uncooked)
2 Tbsp	cornmeal
½ tsp	salt
¼ tsp	cayenne pepper
4 tsp	cornmeal
	cooking spray

PREPARATION

- Sauté corn, onion and thyme in 1 tsp olive oil in large nonstick skillet over medium high heat.
- Place corn mixture, chick peas, breadcrumbs, oats, 2 Tbsp cornmeal, salt and cayenne pepper in food processor. Pulse 8 times or until combined and chunky.
- Divide mixture into 8 portions, shaping into a ½ inch patty. Dredge patties in remaining cornmeal. Heat ½ tsp oil in skillet coated with cooking spray over medium-high heat. Cook each patty 5 minutes, and then carefully turn over. Cook another 4 minutes until golden.

NUTRITIONAL ANALYSIS
Servings: 8
103 calories
4 g. protein
19 g. carbohydrates
2 g. fat
17% calories from fat
27 mg. calcium

Marinated Flank Steak

Charlotte Otto
Global External Relations Officer, P&G

This is a great "Old Faithful" recipe for a dinner party. It's quick and easy with very little kitchen mess. The meat and marinade can even be prepared the day before use.

INGREDIENTS

1 cup	chili sauce (12 oz. bottle)
¼ cup	soy sauce (low sodium)
2 Tbsp	Worcestershire sauce
2 Tbsp	molasses
½ tsp	chili powder
½ tsp	dry minced onion
½ tsp	liquid smoke
¼ tsp	garlic powder
	salt and freshly ground pepper to taste
2-2½ lb.	flank steak (sometimes called marinating steak)

PREPARATION

* Combine first 8 ingredients with salt and pepper. A plastic food bag that zips or seals works great! Place meat in the bag with the marinade and turn until meat is thoroughly coated. Refrigerate a minimum of two hours, preferably overnight.

* Grill or broil meat to desired doneness, turning once and basting often with sauce. About 7 minutes per side is a good place to start. Carve steak by slicing diagonally. Warm the remaining sauce and serve with the steak.

NUTRITIONAL ANALYSIS
Serves 8, each 5 oz. serving contains approximately:
277 calories
32 g. protein
13.5 g. carbohydrates
10 g. fat
32% calories from fat, but...only 13% from saturated fat
24 mg. calcium

Chapter 9

Pretty Is As Pretty Does

"You can take no credit for beauty at 16.
But if you are beautiful at 60, it will be
your soul's own doing."

Marie Stopes

Our recipe for beauty
begins very simply…

Respect It and Protect It!

Think of yourself as a beautiful painting. First you need a good frame – that would be your bones. Then you need a clean canvas – that would be your skin. Then, comes the actual art – that's what the artist brings, and that is your personality, your soul, your spirit, and most importantly, your passion!

*Pretty is as pretty does. You are what you eat. Beauty is more than skin deep…*these popular truisms have been handed down through the generations in many families. Looking and feeling your best means nourishing your body inside and out. In addition to your outlook on life, a healthy diet, and exercise that puts "nature's roses" on your cheeks, you will need to protect and understand your skin.

Like the rest of your body, your skin undergoes some changes as you age. You may begin to notice what women have identified as the signs of aging: fine lines and wrinkles, rough texture, uneven tone, dullness, enlarged pores, dryness, blotches and age spots. Some even find that they begin to have acne again! What can you do? Plenty!

Regardless of your age and past habits, there are ways to turn back the clock…consider over-the-counter micro-dermabrasion products, that come in kits. There are also exfoliating cloths and serums that can help minimize the signs of aging.

First, get off to a good start by knowing that what is good for your body is also good for your skin. That means…

✔ drink plenty of water

✔ get enough rest

✔ maintain a physically active lifestyle

✔ eat a balanced diet low in fat and full of fruits and vegetables

✔ protect with a moisturizer formulated for your skin type

✔ protect from sun's harmful rays, the number one cause of skin damage and wrinkling. Use a sunscreen with a minimum SPF (sun protection factor) of 15 on all exposed areas each and every day. Consider a daily moisturizer or foundation with sunscreen added. And, there are skin care products that can give you a "tan" without exposing your skin to the harmful sun or tanning beds.

What to add to the "recipe" for family skin health…SPF

Did you know? Up to 80% of skin's damage occurs before the age of 18. Start a lifelong habit with your children with sunscreen. Teach them to protect themselves from sun's harmful rays. Children spend a great deal of time in the sun, getting an average of three times more exposure to the sun's rays than adults.

If you use these simple tips to protect yourself and your family, you can significantly reduce skin cancers (and wrinkles that make you look older than you are).

✔ **Always use a sunscreen with a minimum SPF (sun protection factor) of 15.** Apply sunscreen 15 to 30 minutes before you go out. Reapply every 2 to 3 hours, whether you're using a waterproof product or not.

✔ **Limit your time in the sun.** Avoid the sun when it's

strongest, between 10 a.m. and 3 p.m. Remember, up to 70% of sun's rays can still penetrate cloud cover.

✔ **Wear protective clothing and sunglasses.**

✔ **Ask your doctor or pharmacist** if medications you're taking may increase your sensitivity to sunlight and your risk of burning.

✔ **Avoid using harsh products or chemicals on your skin.** Choose a mild soap or bath wash for daily use, and seal moisture by applying a moisturizing cream or lotion all over immediately after bathing, while your skin is still damp. Choose well-tested and researched national brands, with a toll-free number on the packaging. Check the ingredients just as you would if you were eating them.

Finally, you're never fully dressed without a smile. Beauty radiates from within…show the world your beauty with a positive outlook and a healthy smile! A healthy smile begins with a healthy mouth. The ingredients for a healthy mouth include proper dental care – daily brushing, flossing and seeing a dentist twice a year. And, when it comes to your mouth…small changes make a big difference! Whitening your teeth brightens your smile and will dramatically improve your appearance!

The icing on the cake

Experiment with cosmetics to help you enhance, create and refine your dynamic beauty image. There doesn't have to be anything "extreme" about everyday beauty. Today's cosmetics are sensitive to your skin type and special needs, and many are multi-taskers…simply put, there are many options to help you enhance your natural beauty while you protect your skin. Remember how much fun you had as a child creating "art"? Think of cosmetics as the color for your canvas which will allow you to create your masterpiece. Have fun choosing your "day" look, your "evening" look and your "professional" look. Try a new lipstick. Experiment with a new shadow or blush. Add drama with a new eyeshadow and/or eyeliner and mascara.

Adolescent and teen years

This is a great time for young adults to establish lifelong habits of good hygiene, proper cleansing and moisturizing! That's right…even acne-prone teen skin requires moisture.

✔ Choose an oil-free moisturizer for daily use.

✔ Protect with sunscreen on all exposed areas, every day.

✔ Maintain a balanced diet and drink plenty of water…encourage teens to limit high-fat foods and make healthier choices. Be sure to include calcium and Vitamin D to build strong bones.

$\mathscr{B}$eauty through the ages

20s, 30s...take time!

It's during these years that much of your daily focus may be on others – your spouse, children, careers...don't overlook your own skin's needs.

✔ Proper cleansing and moisturizing are essential. You'll see changes as you age...so, choose products that are right for your skin.

✔ If you smoke, STOP! In addition to all of the health reasons, premature wrinkling has been linked to smoking.

✔ Protect daily with sunscreen.

✔ Moisturize, from the inside out, with at least 8 glasses of water daily.

40s, 50s, 60s and beyond!

Now's the time to pamper yourself...you've earned it! Embrace your beauty and make the most of what you've got.

✔ When your skin loses elastin as you age, causing wrinkling...don't worry! Today's products help minimize the signs of aging and protect, and even repair, your skin.

✔ Protect yourself from sun...wear a wide-brimmed hat when gardening, walking or playing outdoors.

✔ Again...moisturize...inside and out!

Mirror, mirror

Your skin reflects your health. It's your body's canvas. Good health and good looks often go hand in hand. For example, some of the key hallmarks of beauty – hair, skin and nails – are also some of the clearest outward indicators of your state of health. How often has a period of illness revealed itself to the world by showing up first as dry skin or lank, brittle hair or unhealthy nails? If you've ever let your diet slip, eating poorly or not eating enough, you may have noticed that your hair and skin are among the first things to suffer.

Good health can lead to radiant looks – if you're taking care of yourself, your body will tell the world!

A "recipe" for healthy skin

New research suggests that a healthier diet may have a complexion connection. But experts aren't taking the idea at face value. New studies suggest that a diet loaded with fruits and veggies may also help reduce wrinkling. It may be the high content of antioxidant vitamins like A, C and E and phytochemicals found in those foods. (As we've said, to avoid wrinkles, the main thing to leave *off* your "menu" is sunlight.)

4 Step Process to Healthy Skin

1. Cleanse
2. Tone
3. Moisturize
4. Protect

Skin Advances

A new form of moisturizer, called a serum, is now available in stores. For younger-looking skin, look for a serum that contains anti-aging ingredients, such as amino-peptides. "Clinical tests have shown that amino-peptides can help repair damaged skin," says Lorna Thomas, MD, dermatologist, Detroit Medical Center. "Some skin moisturizers also contain amino-peptides for daily results. The more concentrated the amino-peptide complex, the more the product will enhance skin's appearance."

ACE it!

Some of the most important nutrients for the skin are antioxidants – these are the nutrients that fight the damaging effects of free radicals, including those free radicals created by exposure to the sun or pollution in the air. Among the best-known antioxidant nutrients are Vitamins A (or beta carotene), C and E, which are also renowned for their benefits to the skin. Antioxidant nutrients, and especially Vitamin E, are also known to support healthy blood circulation, and it is circulation that is ultimately responsible for providing every part of your body with the nutrients it needs. Another important and well-known antioxidant is lycopene, which is found in such plants as red tomatoes.

Your skin also depends on a good supply of its own natural oils, which it uses to maintain moisture and remain supple and soft.

C? Si!

It's true that Vitamin C is found in more than oranges. The abundant Vitamin C in one serving of papaya helps your body form the collagen it needs to keep your skin, bones, teeth, tendons and nails in tip-top shape. Its strong antioxidant qualities help bolster the immune system against infection and assist in wound healing. One third of a papaya contains 100% of your daily Vitamin C requirements. Other "Si" foods….cantaloupe, strawberries and kiwis!

Need a recipe for your crowning glory…hair it is!
Not unlike our skin, it's important to take care of the
hair we're born with. This means choosing products
specifically-formulated for our hair type (oily, normal,
dry) and conditioning it daily to help protect it from
damage due to normal wear and tear. In addition, new
products can actually help "boost" your hair's volume,
control frizz, lend a hand to nature through curling or
straightening, and help color-treated hair maintain its
color longer. Whatever style you prefer, the basics of
beautiful hair are simple…keep it healthy!

"What we eat, without argument, affects the growth and
health of our bodies, including our hair," states Dr.
Lorna Thomas. "If your hair is nourished and cared for
with proper vitamins, minerals, good cleansing and
moisturizing, you will have strong and healthy hair."

Thomas adds, "Healthy hair is dependent on adequate
daily intake of protein, B Vitamins, zinc and iron. In
general, what is good for overall balanced nutrition is
also healthy for your hair."

1. **Eat lots of fresh fruits and vegetables.** Do not
   overcook your vegetables as many valuable vitamins
   and minerals may be lost if over-cooked.

2. **Eat foods rich in B Vitamins.** Fortify your diet with
   natural Vitamin B-complex found in liver, wheat
   germ, nuts, peas and whole grains.

3. **Avoid the excessive intake of animal fats and
   refined carbohydrates such as white sugar, white
   flour and foods made from them.** Replace animal
   fats and hydrogenated fats in your diet with
   unsaturated vegetable oils: corn oil, safflower oil,
   wheat germ oil, olive oil, etc.

6 Signs of Healthy Hair

1. *Strong*
2. *Soft*
3. *Shiny*
4. *Silky*
5. *Less Frizz*
6. *Body*

If you're interested in covering gray hair, lightening, or want a more vibrant color, use a level 3 product.

4. **Include adequate amounts of protein in the diet.** Proteins work to maintain and build new tissues in the body, including new hair follicles. Research has shown that people who follow a dramatically low-protein diet have displayed signs of hair loss.

5. **Avoid smoking.** Smoking constricts the arteries and the small blood capillaries, while slowing down blood circulation.

Need a lift?

If you're interested in giving your current color a boost, and also getting extra body and shine, try a level 2, semi-permanent product. Level 2 products deposit color on your hair, so they increase the size of your hair shaft giving your hair more body. Choose the color of your lightest strand of hair. Level 2 products can not dramatically lighten, so you'll brighten your "all over" color and get extra shine and body. Since the color washes out after 28 shampoos, you're less likely to get a root line.

Level 3 products are permanent and do not wash out. To maintain the color of your hair and shine, use a daily conditioner specially-made for color-treated hair. You may also consider a weekly treatment to moisturize and hydrate.

If hair is dry from exposure to the sun, perming, coloring or everyday brushing damage, try a deep conditioning treatment to fortify your hair and help prevent further damage. Choose a deep treatment that promises to work in one use for manageability and shine.

Thinning Hair is Aging Hair

Many women think thinning hair is not normal, or that it's a man's problem. Some believe that, if their hair is thinning, they must be sick. Temporary conditions such as pregnancy, menopause, medication, diet, or stress can cause hair thinning. But 70% of women who experience hair loss can attribute it to heredity.

The Thinning Process

As you age, heredity, combined with the effects of hormones and age, cause certain hair follicles to get smaller and smaller. This prevents the hair from fulfilling its regular growth process.

Hair Thinning and Ethnic Women

Hair thinning is non-discriminating, meaning that it can happen to all of us regardless of our ethnic backgrounds. In addition to hereditary hair thinning, many African-American women experience other forms of hair loss, which may be due to the use of hair reshaping products (relaxers, straighteners, hot combs) or hair braiding methods.

Taking Action

What can you do to safely regain control of your appearance and make your hair thicker, fuller and easier to style? Depending on the stage of the hair thinning process, there are three options:

1. Minoxidil (2% topical solution) to reverse the thinning process and help stimulate hair growth;
2. a wig or hairpiece;
3. hair transplant surgery.

Hereditary hair thinning is a common part of life for 1 out of every 4 women. Hair loss affects self-esteem.

Women may feel...
embarrassed or devastated

less feminine or less attractive

less likely to succeed in business

socially unacceptable or helpless

like they are losing their youth

less desirable...

But, it doesn't have to be that way! Read "Taking Action" on this page and turn the page for styling tips for thin hair.

A "Recipe" for Styling Thin Hair

✔ Gently massage scalp for 30 seconds each time you shampoo to promote circulation.

✔ Apply a light conditioner to hair ends, rather than at the roots.

✔ Try products specially-formulated to plump up fine hair by retaining moisture.

✔ Choose lightweight styling products that won't weigh hair down.

✔ Apply a little extra styling product to roots for added volume.

✔ When blow drying, towel dry hair first. Don't use highest heat setting.

✔ If you wear a ponytail, avoid using rubber bands.

✔ Try an above-the-shoulder, layered cut to add fullness.

✔ Color or highlight your hair a shade lighter to make hair look full.

Tough as nails

Have you ever wondered why you cannot wear colored nail polish into surgery? It's because your nails tell a great deal about your overall state of health, including how much oxygen is in your blood – a vital sign closely monitored during a medical procedure.

Nails are composed of **keratin** – which is a type of protein and minerals. Nails provide protection for your fingertips and are meant to be strong yet flexible, smooth and glossy. Nail health relies on sufficient supplies of protein, B Vitamins, Vitamin A, calcium, zinc, iodine and iron. When your body isn't receiving enough of these vital nutrients, or doesn't absorb or assimilate them properly, the deficiency may surface on your nails. Abnormal or unhealthy nails may also be the result of injury, a glandular deficiency such as hypo-thyroidism, or a deficiency of certain nutrients. Did you know that frequent hangnails may indicate an inadequate supply of Vitamin C, folic acid and protein?

Friends for life

Give yourself a hand…set aside a little pampering time. Make a pact with a friend to give yourselves a manicure once every two weeks.

We've been cautioned for years to think of our nails as "Jewels, not Tools!" Proper nail care is needed not just so you look good, but is also part of a healthy hygiene routine. Even if you prefer your nails short and natural, a manicure will keep them clean and free from bacteria. Want a fun, pampering treat? Why not get together with your friends for a manicure party. While you're at it, try a pedicure, too…after all, our feet carry the weight of the world!

Now that your hands and feet look beautiful…add a "kick" to a classic Salsa or "toss" a few new ideas into a Spring Salad. See recipes on the following pages.

Spring Salad

Thanks to Lee Anne Mills, Senior Marketing Manager
Wal-Mart

This is a basic recipe for making a healthy tossed salad, but where you take it from here is really up to you…nearly anything can be added in for more flavor and fun!

INGREDIENTS

Mixed greens
can include baby greens, arugula, raddichio, Boston red leaf, baby spinach, romaine, Bibb…anything but iceberg works!
We used 12 cups total greens

Vegetables
we love cherry tomatoes, carrots, celery, chopped fennel (the white part), cucumber, frozen peas, edamame
We used 4 cups veggies

Fruits
try fresh pears, apples, grapes or dried cherries, cranberries, raisins, figs, dates, whatever you have on hand…don't forget the berries…fresh blueberries, raspberries, strawberries
We used 3 cups fruits

Nuts or seeds
sunflower kernels (unsalted!), soy nuts, almonds, walnuts

Cheeses
use sparingly for flavor without adding fat. Consider low-fat varieties of goat, feta, bleu, gorgonzola, asiago. Consider serving separately so it can be lightly sprinkled on the individual salad (you'll use less this way, and keep the fat content to a minimum).

PREPARATION

Toss together in a bowl with your favorite low-fat salad dressing, or try a simple, easy and **healthy vinaigrette**:

½ cup olive oil

¼ cup flavored vinegar – balsamic, apple cider, wine vinegar, raspberry vinegar

Splash of lemon juice

Garlic powder

Combine in a cruet and shake. Refrigerate unused portion for best results.

NUTRITIONAL ANALYSIS (as prepared), serves 12
Each 1-cup serving contains approximately:
271 calories
6 g. protein
20 g. carbohydrates
20 g. fat
66% calories from fat, but…only 14% from saturated fat
124 mg. calcium

Nutritional analysis will vary based on ingredients and amounts used.

Salsa

Thanks to Holly Strauch, Senior Culinary Specialist
Nestle Foods (Stouffer's Lean Cuisine)

Mango Salsa Recipe

INGREDIENTS

1	small mango
1	large tomato, seeded and chopped
$\frac{1}{3}$ cup	chopped red onion
$\frac{1}{4}$ cup	minced fresh cilantro
1	small jalapeño pepper, seeded and finely chopped
2 Tbsp	lime juice

PREPARATION

Carefully peel skin from mango sections attached to seed. Slice flesh from seed. Chop flesh to measure $1\frac{1}{2}$ cups. Combine all ingredients in small bowl; refrigerate 2 hours.

Want a twist on the "classic" salsa? Consider adding raspberries, apricots or even pineapple or mangoes to your recipe. It adds a healthy "kick" and a new taste you're sure to love!

Basic Tomato Salsa

INGREDIENTS

4 to 5	tomatoes
1	shallot, peeled and diced
2	cloves garlic
2 Tbsp	basil
2 tsp	olive oil
2 to 4	green chilies, diced
	salt and black pepper

OTHER VARIATIONS

	add 1 can corn
	canned black beans
1	chopped avocado
$\frac{1}{2}$	fresh lime, squeezed over blended mixture
	minced fresh cilantro

PREPARATION

Combine all ingredients into food processor and process until well blended. Refrigerate at least two to three hours for ingredients to meld. Add extra chilies for more spicy flavor.

NUTRITIONAL ANALYSIS Makes 2 cups, 8 servings
Each 1/4 cup serving contains approximately:
32 calories
1 g. protein
5 g. carbohydrates
1 g. fat
28% calories from fat
18 mg. calcium
Nutritional analysis will vary based on ingredients used.

Chapter 10

Healthy Screenings

"All life is an experiment. The more experiments you make the better."

Ralph Waldo Emerson

*Our recipe for developing a passion
about your good health, begins very simply…*

Know the
Appropriate Health
Screenings…

Use the chart at the end of this chapter to begin a dialogue with your doctor about what's appropriate for your age. Take the time to schedule these screenings. Just getting them on your calendar, relieves the stress of wondering if you are in good health. Having a scheduled appointment will create a definite time for you to talk to your doctor about specific health concerns. Knowing the results of the tests will arm you with an action plan for health. Hopefully all of the results will be fine and you will be encouraged to do more of what you've been doing. As we say at Speaking of Women's Health, "Nothing motivates like success".

Often, when we think of screenings, we think only of PAP tests, mammograms, colonoscopies, etc. These are critically important to your health and we will discuss all of these types of screenings in this chapter. But, before we do, let's talk about the most basic screening…the annual physical with your doctor or other health care provider.

In Chapter 6 we've talked about relationships…one of the most important relationships you'll have in life is the one with your doctor and other health care professionals. It's important to feel confident about your health care team and to build a "healthy" relationship that makes you a primary partner in your medical decisions.

How to have a "healthy" appointment with your doctor

Once you've established a relationship with a doctor you trust and with whom you're comfortable, remember that maintaining your health is a two-way relationship. Follow these steps to make the most of the time you have scheduled with your doctor.

Get comfortable. Discuss your concerns the way you would with a trusted friend.

Put it in black and white. Write down your questions ahead of time and bring the list to each appointment.

Request a longer appointment at the time you call to schedule. Be sure to let the receptionist know if you have serious issues to discuss with your doctor.

Do your homework. Do research about your condition and treatment options. Partner with your doctor to determine the most accurate, up-to-date information, tests, diagnoses and advice.

Your pharmacist... a key member of your team

A trusted pharmacist may be a great place to start asking questions about over-the-counter and prescription medications, as well as vitamins, supplements, herbs and other healthful resources. It's important to let your doctor or pharmacist know what herbs and vitamins you take to help guard against potentially-dangerous drug interactions.

New medicine? Be sure to ask:

✔ How often should I take it? Does 3 times a day mean around the clock?

✔ Empty stomach or not? Is this medicine tolerated easier when taken after food? Will this medicine be less effective if I have eaten recently?

✔ What if I miss a dose? Should I wait until the next dose? Should I take it as soon as I remember and then wait the appropriate amount of time? Would there ever be a reason to "double-up" on the dosage?

✔ What are possible side effects? Might this make me nauseous, sleepy, dizzy, etc.?

✔ Am I at risk for food or drug interactions? Tell your physician AND your pharmacist about ANY and ALL medications you are taking, including prescriptions, over-the-counter, herbs or vitamins, etc.

Get screened, and stay that way!

Here's some great news! Early detection of most illnesses definitely increases the opportunity for successful treatment. Many cancers, once thought to be deadly, are now treatable – but, early detection is the key. Maintain a positive working relationship with your physician. Know your risk factors for heart disease, breast, gynecologic and colorectal cancers, diabetes and osteoporosis. Take advantage of technology and get screened according to the timetable that you and your doctor agree upon. In addition to a mammogram, perform a monthly breast self-exam, or even better... research now suggests that even more frequent examinations of the breasts, underarms and lymph nodes may be better. Any change in what is "usual" should be reported to your doctor. ***The better we know our bodies, the greater our chance for detecting the unusual.*** Also, many cases of breast cancers have been detected by a woman's partner. Be sure to have a caring conversation with your partner about letting you know of ANY difference he may notice in your body. Besides being the "love of your life", he may "save your life"!

It's also important to talk to your doctor about a C-Reactive Protein (CRP) test. It's an inexpensive blood test that has shown to be a promising indicator of inflammation. Increased levels of C-Reactive Protein in the blood indicate that inflammation is present, which may lead to arterial blockages, and, most recently, as a predictor of colon cancer. For more information on CRP, see page 23.

As always, annual screenings, partnering with your health care team as well as knowing your family history, are essential "ingredients" for *your* "recipes for living well". Don't forget to allow yourself some special indulgences. We've saved these recipes, which honor ethnic family heritage, for the last chapter...ENJOY!

We hope you keep this book in your kitchen and refer to it often. Please let us hear from you about how this book helped you make positive changes, and...send us *your* favorite "recipes for living well" to www.speakingofwomenshealth.com.

AGE APPROPRIATE PREVENTIVE CARE TABLE

Health Activity	Ages 18-39	Ages 40-49	
Physical Exam	annually	annually	
Blood Pressure/Pulse	every other year	every year	
Eye & Ear Exam	baseline by 39	every 2-4 years	
Dental Exam	twice a year	twice a year	
Skin Exam	every 2 years	every year	
IMMUNIZATIONS			
Tetanus/Diphtheria	every 10 years	every 10 years	
Influenza (Flu)	per risk	per risk	
Measles/Mumps/Rubella	up to date	usually not needed	
Pneumonia Vaccine	usually not needed	usually not needed	
Cholesterol/Triglycerides	at age 20	every 5 years	
Blood Sugar Evaluation (Diabetes)	usually not needed	every 3 years at 45	
Bone Density for Osteoporosis	usually not needed	usually not needed	
BREAST CANCER SCREENING			
Breast Self-Exam	teach BSE by age 20	monthly	
Mammography	usually not needed	annually	
Breast Exam by Physician	every 1-3 years	annually	
CERVICAL CANCER SCREENING			
Pap Test	annually	annually	
Pelvic Exam by Physician	annually	annually	
COLON CANCER SCREENING			
Fecal Occult Blood Test and/or;	usually not needed	usually not needed	
Flexible Sigmoidoscopy or;	usually not needed	usually not needed	
Colonoscopy or;	usually not needed	usually not needed	
Double Contrast Barium Enema	usually not needed	usually not needed	

Screening tests are used to identify a disease previously unrecognized, or the risk factors associated with a particular disease. A number of health care organizations publish guidelines for the use of screening tests in certain age groups. These guidelines may vary or change from time to time because of new research or differences in interpretation by different health care organizations.

* Your health care team can assist you in adopting screening tests that apply to your particular family history.
   (G. Byron Kallam, MD offers this chart as a place to begin a dialogue with your health care team.)

	Ages 50-64	Age 65+	Comments
	annually	annually	as needed with health demands
	every year	every year	more often with family history
	every 2-4 years; 60+ yearly	yearly	more frequent visits with problems
	twice a year	twice a year	as needed with changes in dental health
	every year	every year	as needed with changes in skin
	every 10 years	every 10 years	
	yearly	yearly	pregnancy, lung disease and heart disease require immunization prior to age 50
	usually not needed	usually not needed	immunity desired prior to pregnancy
	usually not needed	at age 65	booster may be required in 5 years
	every 5 years	every 5 years	more frequent if abnormality detected
	every 3 years	every 3 years	*more frequent and earlier depending on risk level and family history
	baseline if at risk	age 65	*may screen earlier with risk factors
	monthly	monthly	always call physician with concerns
	annually	annually	risk level may require higher frequency
	annually	annually	*risk level may require higher frequency
	annually	annually	*some doctors feel that after three or more consecutive normal results, Pap smears may be performed every 2-3 years on certain low-risk women
	annually	annually	
	annually	annually	
	every 3-5 years	every 3-5 years	*colon screening may be performed earlier and more frequently with certain risk factors and family history
	every 5 years	every 5 years	
	every 5 years	every 5 years	

Aji de Gallina
Spicy Peruvian Chicken

Thanks to Inés Barranca
Senior Creative Consultant
Hispanic Markets
American Greetings

We've varied this traditional Peruvian recipe just slightly for a healthier meal. This one-of-a-kind recipe is an authentic treat your family will love!

INGREDIENTS

¼ cup	soy sauce (low sodium)
2	chicken breasts, with or without breast bone
1 cup	water
½ cup	evaporated skim (non-fat) milk
5 slices	white bread
⅓ cup	chunky peanut butter
1 cup	parmesan cheese
4	garlic cloves
4 Tbsp	yellow pepper paste
½ tsp	tumeric (may substitute curry powder)
2 tsp	cumin
1 tsp	black pepper
	salt to taste
¼ cup	oil
6	Yukon gold potatoes

NUTRITIONAL ANALYSIS, with potatoes
Serves: 6
580 calories
45 g. protein
45 g. carbohydrates
25 g. fat
39% calories from fat, but...only 10% from saturated
  fat
352 mg. calcium

PREPARATION

- Boil chicken breasts in water in small pan, add a pinch of salt. When cooked, place chicken breasts aside and let them cool before shredding them. Do not discard chicken broth.

- Place bread in medium bowl, add milk and ½ cup chicken broth. Place in blender and blend in low speed until bread is the consistency of oatmeal. Add chicken broth or milk as necessary.

- In stewing pan, sauté onion, yellow pepper paste, minced garlic, black pepper, cumin, tumeric until onion is translucent. Immediately add the bread mixture, shredded chicken, peanut butter, salt and parmesan cheese. Stir until well blended. If mixture is too thick, add chicken broth. If you like it spicier, add yellow pepper paste.

- Serve hot over thick potato slices. May be served with long grain white rice.

Marsala Winter Vegetables

Thanks to Katie Taylor
Chief Customer Officer, Sara Lee Branded Apparel (Hanes Her Way)

INGREDIENTS

¼ cup	soy sauce (low sodium)
3 cups	½ inch cubed peeled rutabaga
1⅓ cups	½ inch thick sliced parsnip
1½ cups	pearl onions, peeled
1 cup	sliced carrots
1½ cups	trimmed halved Brussels sprouts
	cooking spray
1 Tbsp	butter
1 Tbsp	extra-virgin olive oil
2 tsp	chopped fresh thyme or
1 tsp	dried thyme
	salt and pepper to taste
⅛ tsp	ground nutmeg
1 cup	dry Marsala wine

PREPARATION

- Preheat oven to 450 degrees.

- Bring 2 quarts water to boil in a Dutch oven. Add the rutabaga, parsnip, onions and carrot; cook 4 minutes. Add Brussels sprouts and cook 1 minute.

- Drain and place vegetables in a large roasting or jelly roll pan coated with cooking spray. Add butter and the next 5 ingredients, stirring mixture until butter melts. Pour wine over vegetables, cover pan with foil.

- Bake vegetables for 30 minutes. Uncover and stir vegetables (do not remove pan from oven). Bake an additional 15 minutes or until vegetables are tender, stirring after 8 minutes.

NUTRITIONAL ANALYSIS
Serves: 10
Each serving contains approximately:
108 calories
2 g. protein
15 g. carbohydrates
3 g. fat
25% calories from fat
73 mg. calcium

Index

Acid 90-92

Actonel® 37

Aerobic Activity 49, 53

Alendronate 37-38

Allergies (food) 93, 96

Amino-peptides 122

Anthocyanins................................13-15, 29

Antioxidants 15, 26, 29, 122

Apple Crisp (recipe) 85

Aspirin...28

Bacteria 93-94, 97, 127

Balance (physical) 29, 40, 118-119

Balance (emotional) 2, 65-66, 103, 108-109

Barium Enema 95, 136-137

Beta-Carotene 12, 14

Beauty...117-123

Biotin...12, 29

Bipolar Disorder 64, 70

Bisphosphonates....................................37-38

Blood Pressure..............9, 22, 25, 27-28, 39, 47-48, 64, 69, 136-137

BLT Salad (recipe) 59

Blueberry Burgers (recipe) 17

Blueberry Cobbler (recipe) 19

Bone(s) 8, 34-41, 136

Bone Density 36, 38, 136-137

Breast Cancer................21, 28, 80, 136-137

Breast Self-Exam 135-137

Breathing.........................25, 65, 96, 106

Brown Rice Medley (recipe) 101

Caffeine 68, 90, 109

Calcitonin 37

Calcium 8, 12, 14, 26, 35-37, 39-41, 68-69, 94, 96, 119, 127

Cancer..........11, 14, 15, 21, 23, 27, 28, 135

Carbohydrates 7-9, 12-13, 55, 123

Cardiovascular Disease 28

Chick Pea and Corn Patties (recipe) 113

Chicken Cacciatore (recipe) 73

Chocolate 2, 81-83, 92-93

Chocolate Mint Cake (recipe) 87

Cholesterol ..2, 8-9, 22, 27-29, 48, 136-137

Colon Cancer................23, 47, 95, 135-137

Colonoscopy 95, 133, 136-137

Constipation 93-94

C-Reactive Protein (CRP) 23, 135

Dairy Products 7-8, 11-12, 14, 26, 96

Dehydration 54-55

Depression 28, 47, 64, 67-70, 106

DEXA-Scan 36-37

Diabetes 11, 13, 22, 47, 135

Esophagus 90-92

Estrogen(s) 36-38, 41, 81

Evista® 37

Exercise...................2, 7, 22, 24, 37, 39-40, 46-57, 64-69, 103, 105, 109, 117

Fats................................7, 9, 11, 13, 27, 123

Fecal Occult Blood Test...........95, 136-137

Fiber 8-9, 13-14, 22, 26-27, 94

Fish 7-9, 11-14, 27

Flexibility...50, 69

Folate 13-14

Food Allergy(ies) 93, 96

Food Reaction 96

Forteo® 38

Fosamax® 37

Friends, Friendships 2, 22, 25, 67, 69-70, 76-78, 83, 107-108, 127

Fruits 7, 9, 11-15, 24-26, 29, 92, 94, 118, 121, 123

Index

Gas 89, 93, 97

Gastroesophageal Reflux Disease
(GERD) 91-92

Grain(s) 7, 9, 11-14, 26, 96, 123

Guacamole Dip 31

Gut 88-97

Hair................................108, 121, 123-126

Hair Color 54, 124, 126

Hair Loss..............................80, 124-125

Heart 2, 7-9, 11, 13, 15,
20-29, 39, 47-49, 53, 63-64, 77, 79-81,
83, 91, 103, 135, 136-137

Heart Attack 22-23, 25, 28, 77, 91

Heart Disease 2, 8-9, 11, 13, 15, 21-24,
27-29, 47, 64, 135, 136-137

Heart Health 22, 81

Heartburn.......................................89-93

Hydration 54

Indigestion...89

Iron 8, 12, 94, 123, 127

Irritable Bowel Syndrome (IBS) 89-90

Journal(ing) 66, 106, 109

Keratin...127

Legumes 8, 11-14, 27

Lentil Soup (recipe) 45

Libido/Desire 81, 83

Lycopene 13-15, 122

Mac & Cheese (recipe)............................43

Magnesium 13, 29

Mammogram(s) 133, 135-137

Manganese...12

Marinated Flank Steak (recipe) 115

Marsala Winter Vegetables (recipe) 141

Massage 54, 108

Meat................................8, 11, 26-27, 111

Medication(s) 6, 9, 36-38, 64, 67, 90-92,
94, 119, 125, 134

Memory 15, 29, 48, 63-64

Menopause 36, 94, 125

Mental Health 62-71

Mental Illness 70

Mercury 27

Micro-dermabrasion 118

Minerals 7-9, 29, 123, 127

Mono-unsaturated Fats 9, 13, 29

Moisturizer(s) 118-119, 122

Nail(s) 108, 121-122, 127

Niacin 8, 12, 29

Nutrition 5, 7, 10, 103, 106, 110, 123

Omega-3 Fatty Acids 8-9, 13, 27

Omega-6 Fatty Acids 8-9

Osteopenia...36

Osteoporosis 2, 11, 35-39, 49, 135-137

Pampering 103, 107, 109, 127

Pantothenic Acid 12, 29

Pap Test 133, 136-137

Parathyroid Hormone (PTH) 37-38

Pedometer 49, 52

Peruvian Chicken (recipe) 139

Pharmacist 92-96, 119, 134

Phytochemicals 8, 121

Phytoestrogens...12

Polypeptides...38

Polyps...95

Poly-unsaturated Fats 9

Pork Loin with Cherry Stuffing (recipe)..99

Portion (serving size) 8, 10-11, 26-27

Potassium 12-13, 26, 29

Progesterone 81

Index

Prostate Cancer 8, 15

Protein 7-8, 23, 27, 29, 41, 123-124, 127, 135

Raloxifene 37

Rectum 95

Reflux 91-92

Relationships 70, 76-83, 103, 105, 133

Relaxation 47, 65, 104-106

Risedronate 37-38

Salmon (recipe)......................................33

Salsa(s) (recipes) 131

Sandwich Generation 102, 104, 105,

Schizophrenia 64, 70

Screenings 2, 22-23, 103-104, 132-137

Self-Esteem 66, 77, 106, 125

Shoes 38, 56

Sigmoidoscopy 95, 136-137

Shrimp Pasta (recipe) 61

Skin 8, 108, 117-123, 136-137

Sleep 23, 48, 64, 67, 103-104, 106, 109

Smile 119

Smoking 22, 28, 39, 41, 90, 120, 124

Sodium 27, 41

SPF..40, 118

Spring Salad (recipe) 129

Stress 2, 22-23, 25, 48, 64-65, 68-69, 90, 104-106, 125, 133

Stretching 50, 53

Sun 40, 69, 118-120, 122, 124

Sunscreen 69, 118-120

Swimming....................40, 48-49, 51-52, 56

Synapses...63

Tension...................................25, 48, 64-65

Teriparatide 38

Testosterone..39, 81

Thanksgiving Day Turkey (recipe) 75

Trans Fatty Acids 9, 27

US Center for Mental Health Services 69

US Food & Drug Administration........9, 37

Vegetables............4, 7, 9, 11-14, 26, 29, 41, 94, 118, 123

Vitamin A 12, 106, 121-122, 127

Vitamin B 123, 127

Vitamin B6 ....12-13, 70

Vitamin B12 70

Vitamin C............13-14, 106, 121-122, 127

Vitamin D 12, 37, 39-40, 69, 119

Vitamin E 13-14, 29, 106, 121-122

Vitamin K 12, 29

Vitamins 7-9, 11, 29, 106, 121-123, 127, 134

Walking 24, 40, 48-49, 52-54, 56-57, 108, 120

Water 7-8, 10, 54-55, 94, 118-120

Weight..................10, 22, 27, 39-40, 48-51, 54, 90, 95

Weight-bearing Exercises 40, 49-50

Weight-lifting 49

Yoga 25, 50, 68-69, 106

Yogurt..........................8, 11, 26, 40-41, 97

Zinc 12, 123, 127